ACE Personal Trainer

Master the Manual

A Study Guide to Accompany the
ACE Personal Trainer Manual

Fourth Edition

D1385048

AMERICAN COUNCIL ON EXERCISE

4851 Paramount Drive, San Diego, California 92123, 800-825-3636, www.acefitness.org

Distributed by:
American Council on Exercise
4851 Paramount Dr.
San Diego, CA 92123
(858) 576-6500
FAX (858) 576-6564
www.acefitness.org

Project Editor: Daniel J. Green
Technical Editor: Cedric X. Bryant, Ph.D., FACSM
Cover Design & Art Direction: Karen McGuire
Associate Editor: Marion Webb
Special Contributors & Proofreaders: Sabrena Merrill, M.S. & Todd Galati, M.A.
Production: Nancy Garcia
Anatomical Illustrations: James Staunton

P12-006

TABLE OF CONTENTS

How to Use This Study Guide

Welcome to *Master the Manual,* a study guide designed as a companion to the *ACE Personal Trainer Manual,* 4th Edition. The exercises in this book will help you master the basics of personal training by breaking them into manageable concepts that you can then apply to real-life situations.

Each chapter of the study guide is divided into sections. **Getting Started** introduces you to the material, providing objectives to concentrate on as you read the corresponding chapter in the manual. **Expand Your Knowledge** will test your comprehension through a variety of exercises and drills. **Show What You Know** exercises your ability to apply what you have learned to real-life situations. Some chapters will take you one step further, providing activities to further expand your skills in **Practice What You Know.** If you are using the *ACE Personal Trainer Manual* in conjunction with this study guide to prepare for the ACE Personal Trainer Certification Examination, you should focus not only on learning the concepts, but also on applying them to practical training situations. Finally, each chapter includes 10 multiple-choice questions that mirror the style and difficulty level of questions seen on the actual ACE exam.

Step One: Read

Read the student objectives for each chapter, then read the corresponding chapter in the *ACE Personal Trainer Manual.* Read one chapter at a time and be sure that you have mastered those concepts before moving on to the next chapter. As you read, look for the boldface vocabulary words.

Step Two: Define

After you have read each chapter, define the vocabulary words on a separate piece of paper. Write the definition even if you feel you already know it. Learning is a sensory experience, so the more senses you can involve in the learning process, the more you will be able to retain. Writing down definitions, or putting your thoughts into words, will help you remember the material more clearly.

Step Three: Exercises

After defining the vocabulary words, skim the chapter in the manual again. Attempt to do the exercises in the *Master the Manual* without looking at the manual. Check your answers against the key that appears in Appendix B, which begins on page 172. If you answer a question incorrectly, go back to the text and find out why your answer is wrong. Make a note to yourself for future reference. If you answered a question correctly, but feel you were guessing, go back to the manual and read that section again. Do not assume you will remember it.

Step Four: Final Notes

Now is the time to go back to the objectives on the first page of each *Master the Manual* chapter. Mark any areas you are unsure of or want to learn more about, and reread the related sections in the manual. Refer to the references and suggested reading lists at the end of each manual chapter to find sources for more information.

The focus of this study guide is on learning and retention. That is why we do not grade the exercises or relate the results to either a score or to your chance for success on the ACE exam. No textbook or study guide can predict your performance on a certification examination. If you feel you need additional preparation, you may contact ACE at www.acefitness.org or 800-825-3636 to get information on ACE exam preparation training programs.

CHAPTER 1

Role and Scope of Practice for the Personal Trainer

Summary Review

Personal trainers must be prepared to work with clients ranging in age from youth to older adults, and ranging in health and fitness status from overweight and sedentary to athletic.

Personal trainers should have a solid understanding of the research linking physical activity to health, as well as knowledge of guidelines for physical activity, such as the *2008 Physical Activity Guidelines for Americans* developed by the U.S. Department of Health & Human Services.

The Allied Healthcare Continuum

Personal trainers should understand the roles of the professionals in the following specialty areas within allied healthcare, as well as the role of fitness professionals in relation to other members of the healthcare team:
- Physicians/nurse practitioners
- Rehabilitation professionals
- Nutritional support
- Mental health practitioners
- Alternative healthcare (licensed) professionals
- Trainers/instructors

The ACE Personal Trainer Certification

A qualified and effective ACE-certified Personal Trainer has an understanding of the following concepts:
- Definition of "scope of practice"
- Scope of practice for ACE-certified Personal Trainers
- Knowledge, skills, and abilities of the ACE-certified Personal Trainer
- Education and experience required to service clients
- Preparation recommendations and testing requirements for sitting for the ACE Personal Trainer Exam Certification
- Professional responsibilities and ethics
  - ✓ ACE Code of Ethics
  - ✓ ACE Professional Practices and Disciplinary Procedures
  - ✓ Certification period and renewal
  - ✓ Client privacy
  - ✓ Referral
  - ✓ Safety
  - ✓ Supplements
  - ✓ Ramifications of offering services outside the scope of practice

Accreditation of Allied Healthcare Credentials

The ACE-certified Personal Trainer should understand the importance of third-party accreditation from a credible organization like the National Commission for Certifying Agencies, as well as the following concepts related to the advancement of personal training within the allied healthcare environment:

- Recognition from the fitness and health industry
- Recognition from the education community
- Recognition from the department of labor

Career Development

Every personal trainer should have a general idea of the career path that he or she wants to follow. After setting a career plan, a personal trainer can use it as a template for researching and selecting continuing education to work toward his or her goals by understanding the opportunities available in the following areas:

- Continuing education
  - ✓ Advanced knowledge
  - ✓ Specialization
- Degrees
- Additional fitness certifications
- New areas of expertise within allied healthcare

Getting Started

This chapter introduces the role of the ACE-certified Personal Trainer within the healthcare community and provides guidelines for staying within the defined scope of practice. This chapter also covers safety concerns in a fitness facility, as well as consultation and privacy issues. After completing this chapter, you will have a better understanding of:

- The knowledge, skills, and abilities associated with being a successful personal trainer
- The ACE Code of Ethics
- ACE's Professional Practices and Disciplinary Procedures
- How the ACE certification has received recognition from the fitness and health industry, the education community, and the department of labor
- The importance of a career-development plan

Reading Assignment

Read Chapter 1 of the *ACE Personal Trainer Manual,* 4th edition, paying special attention to the boldface terms in the chapter. After you have read the chapter, define those terms on a separate piece of paper.

Expand Your Knowledge

I. List the eight research findings regarding physical activity and its associated health benefits included in the *2008 Physical Activity Guidelines for Americans*.

a. _____

_____

b. _____

_____

c. _____

_____

d. _____

_____

e. _____

_____

f. _____

_____

g. _____

_____

h. _____

_____

II. What differentiates the *2008 Physical Activity Guidelines for Americans* from guidelines and recommendations previously published by the U.S. government? _____

_____

_____

_____

_____

_____

_____

III. List the six reasons why the U.S. Department of Labor expects the employment of fitness workers to increase between 2006 and 2016 more quickly than the average for all occupations.

a. _____

_____

b. _____

_____

c. _____

_____

d. _____

_____

e. _____

_____

f. _____

_____

IV. Fill in the blanks.

a. _____ teach patients the importance of implementing their treatment plans.

b. _____ lead patients through therapeutic exercise and teach them to perform additional exercises at home to facilitate rehabilitation.

c. _____ teach athletes exercises to prevent injury and take them through therapeutic exercises following injury.

d. _____ teach clients proper nutrition through recipes, meal plans, food-preparation methods, and implementation of specialized diets.

V. List the nine principles of conduct included in the ACE Code of Ethics that ACE-certified Professionals are guided by as they interact with clients, the public, and other health and fitness professionals.

a. _____

b. _____

c. _____

d. _____

e. _____

f. _____

g. _____

h. _____

i. _____

VI. Define "scope of practice." _____

_____

_____

VII. List three possible ramifications for ACE-certified Professionals who allow their certifications to expire.

a. _____

b. _____

c. _____

VIII. Review the following client scenarios and write an (A) if the personal trainer's response is appropriate or an (I) if the personal trainer's response is inappropriate.

a. A client has sore shoulders following a long weekend of painting in his home.

Response: _____ The trainer discusses proper technique for icing the shoulders.

b. A client tells the trainer that she is depressed and tired because she was up late fighting with her husband.

Response: _____ The trainer discusses the situation with his or her boss and makes recommendations for improving the situation.

c. A client tells the trainer that he is going to try the Atkins® diet in order to lose weight for his wedding, which is two months away.

Response: _____ The trainer helps the client understand the recommendations and offers tips and recipes to help him get started on the diet.

d. A client wants to purchase amino-acid supplements at the club to take as part of his marathon-training program and asks the trainer for his or her opinion.

Response: _____ The trainer tells the client that amino-acid supplements may enhance endurance and delay fatigue, and probably would help with his training program.

e. The trainer notices that a client stands with a lordotic posture and notes that the client has displayed a weak core in previous workouts.

Response: _____ The trainer implements a program to improve strength and flexibility in the core.

IX. List four factors that should be considered when selecting continuing education courses.

a. _____

b. _____

c. _____

d. _____

Multiple-choice Questions

1. The **PRIMARY** purpose of professional certifications is to _____.
   A. Provide the professional with additional education to enhance his or her knowledge, skills, and abilities
   B. Enhance a professional's resume for employment and/or higher compensation
   C. Protect the public from harm by assessing if candidates meet established levels of minimum competence
   D. Confirm a candidate's understanding of key concepts following the completion of a bachelor's degree

2. Which of the following is **WITHIN** the scope of practice for personal trainers?
   A. Counseling clients through life experiences that negatively impact program adherence
   B. Screening clients for exercise limitations to facilitate exercise program design
   C. Evaluating client injuries while designing rehabilitative exercise programs
   D. Recommending effective supplements for clients who skip meals

3. Which of the following is **OUTSIDE** of the ACE-certified Personal Trainer scope of practice?
   A. Developing exercise programs for clients who have type 2 diabetes and medical clearance for exercise
   B. Providing guidance, motivation, and feedback to empower individuals to adhere to their exercise programs
   C. Implementing post-rehabilitative exercise programs for clients following their physicians' recommendations
   D. Conducting a $\dot{V}O_2$max test to determine a client's need for referral to his or her physician

4. At what point does a candidate for the ACE Personal Trainer Certification (or any other ACE certification) agree to uphold the ACE Code of Ethics?
   A. While registering for an ACE certification exam
   B. Once the candidate earns his or her first ACE certification
   C. Upon receiving a printed copy of the ACE Code of Ethics with the printed ACE certification
   D. When accepting his or her first job as an ACE-certified Personal Trainer

5. ACE-certified Personal Trainers must complete a minimum of 20 hours of continuing education every two years to maintain their certifications. The **PRIMARY** reason ACE has established this minimum continuing-education requirement is to help ACE Personal Trainers to _____.
   A. Earn promotions so they can advance their careers
   B. Increase their earning potential by adding new specialty certificates to their resumes
   C. Enhance their resumes to attract more clients
   D. Stay current with the latest exercise science research and guidelines for fitness and health

6. Which of the following is **WITHIN** the ACE-certified Personal Trainer scope of practice?
    A. Helping clients gain a better understanding of portion sizes and healthful foods so they can make better choices
    B. Providing clients with recipes and shopping lists for four weeks to get them on track with healthful eating
    C. Conducting 24-hour dietary recalls to help clients learn where they have micronutrient deficiencies
    D. Educating clients about resting metabolic rate (RMR) and the need to consume fewer calories than RMR to lose weight

7. A personal trainer who wants to provide massage to help clients who have tight or sore muscles can do so **ONLY** if _____.
    A. The personal trainer has extensive knowledge about the benefits of massage
    B. The client gives his or her consent for the massage
    C. The personal trainer becomes a licensed massage therapist
    D. The massage therapist is not available and the personal trainer has some training

8. What do the credentials for registered dietitians (R.D.), occupational therapists (OTR), athletic trainers (ATC), registered nurses (RN), and massage therapists (LMT) all have in common with certifications from the American Council on Exercise?
    A. Each of them requires a bachelor's degree as a minimum eligibility requirement
    B. They are all accredited by the National Commission for Certifying Agencies
    C. All of them require CPR, AED, and first aid as eligibility requirements
    D. As allied healthcare professions, they share the same scope of practice

9. Which of the following is **MOST** accurate regarding personal trainers recommending supplements to their clients?
    A. The personal trainer should only recommend those supplements covered under his or her professional liability insurance
    B. Unless the personal trainer has other credentials such as an R.D. or M.D., he or she does not possess the qualifications to legally recommend supplements
    C. The personal trainer should become educated about the specific supplements before making any recommendations
    D. Due to potential complications from taking supplements with other medications, personal trainers should recommend only plant-based supplements

10. ACE-certified Personal Trainers looking to advance their knowledge, skills, and abilities beyond their ACE Personal Trainer Certification would be **BEST** served by earning which of the following additional certifications?
    A. A second NCCA-accredited personal-trainer certification
    B. A certification covering sports nutrition and supplementation from a fitness industry organization
    C. An additional personal-training certification from an organization that is not NCCA-accredited
    D. An advanced fitness certification (e.g., ACE-AHFS, ACE-LWMC) that is NCCA-accredited

CHAPTER 2

Principles of Adherence and Motivation

Summary Review

Fitness professionals have a significant challenge in getting people motivated to start—and then stick with—an exercise program. Personal trainers must learn to maximize the experiences of their clients by enhancing motivation, which leads to increased exercise adherence.

Factors Influencing Exercise Participation and Adherence

The potential determinants for physical activity can be broken down into three categories:

- Personal attributes
  - ✓ Demographic variables (education, income, age, and gender)
  - ✓ Biomedical status
  - ✓ Activity history
  - ✓ Psychological traits (self-motivation)
  - ✓ Knowledge, attitudes, and beliefs (locus of control)
- Environmental factors
  - ✓ Access to facilities
  - ✓ Time
  - ✓ Social support
  - ✓ The physical activity itself
- Physical-activity factors
  - ✓ Intensity
  - ✓ Injury

Understanding Motivation

Two commonly discussed approaches for evaluating motivation are intrinsic and extrinsic motivation and self-efficacy.

Intrinsic and Extrinsic Motivation

Most clients fall somewhere on the continuum between being intrinsically and extrinsically motivated. Personal trainers should strive to increase a client's situational motivation and empower the client with the perception of control of his or her own participation.

Self-efficacy

By being aware of self-efficacy levels, personal trainers can consistently motivate clients and help them create positive self-belief.

Feedback

Types of feedback include:

- Intrinsic
- Extrinsic

Leadership Qualities

The components of being an effective leader include:
- Professionalism
- Client–trainer trust
- The ability to listen effectively
- Excitement for the profession
- Genuine concern for the client

The Personal Trainer's Role in Building Adherence

A personal trainer must be able to effectively build adherence by understanding his or her role in the following areas:
- Program design
- Role clarity
- Goal setting
- Contracts/agreements

Strategies to Maintain Client Motivation

Personal trainers can enact strategies to maintain client motivation by effectively educating clients about:
- Relapse prevention
- Social support
- Assertiveness
- Self-regulation
- High-risk situations

Getting Started

This chapter describes the factors that influence exercise adherence and methods for keeping clients involved in their exercise programs. After completing this chapter, you will have a better understanding of:
- The factors influencing exercise adherence
- The difference between intrinsic and extrinsic motivation
- Leadership qualities that affect exercise adherence
- The personal trainer's role in building adherence
- The importance of role clarity in establishing the client–trainer relationship
- Properly worded and structured goals

Reading Assignment

Read Chapter 2 of the *ACE Personal Trainer Manual*, 4th edition, paying special attention to the boldface terms in the chapter. After you have read the chapter, define those terms on a separate piece of paper.

Expand Your Knowledge

I. Fill in the blanks.
    a. _____ is a complex construct that refers to the psychological drive that gives behavior direction and purpose.
    b. More than _____% of people who start a new exercise program will drop out within the first six months.
    c. _____ refers to voluntary and active involvement in an exercise program.
    d. _____ is arguably the most important and influential personal attribute variable when predicting the likelihood of program adherence.

II. Factors influencing exercise participation and adherence are classified as personal (P), environmental (E), or physical-activity (A) factors. Place the appropriate letter beside each of the following factors.
    a. _____ Biomedical status
    b. _____ Activity history
    c. _____ Time
    d. _____ Intensity
    e. _____ Demographic variables
    f. _____ Injury
    g. _____ Knowledge, attitudes, and beliefs
    h. _____ Social support
    i. _____ Psychological traits
    j. _____ Access to facilities

III. Explain how each of the following factors might influence an individual client's likelihood of sticking with an exercise program.
    a. Locus of control
    _____
    _____
    _____

    b. Social support
    _____
    _____
    _____

    c. Intensity
    _____
    _____
    _____

IV. List four ways in which a personal trainer can enhance the feelings of enjoyment and accomplishment that come with program participation (i.e., situational motivation).
    a. _____
    b. _____
    c. _____
    d. _____

V.   Define self-efficacy as it relates to physical activity.

_____

_____

VI.   List five components of effective leadership.

    a. _____

    b. _____

    c. _____

    d. _____

    e. _____

VII. Answer the following questions about goal setting.

    a. What are the five components of SMART goal setting?_____

_____

_____

    b. Why is setting positively worded goals so important? _____

_____

_____

    c. How often should clients be achieving short-term goals?_____

_____

_____

    d. What is the most important thing that a trainer can do to maximize the effectiveness of the goal-setting process? _____

_____

_____

Multiple-choice Questions

1. What is the **MOST** important factor for an individual who is starting an exercise program?
   A. Strong support from family and friends
   B. Convenience of the exercise facility
   C. Readiness to change behavior related to exercise
   D. Connecting with a personal trainer

2. Which personal attribute is the **MOST** reliable predictor of an individual's participation in an exercise program?
   A. Weight
   B. Past exercise program participation
   C. Age
   D. Perceived time barriers

3. What is the **MOST** common excuse used by people when dropping out of an exercise program?
   A. Limited access to the exercise facility
   B. A lack of support
   C. Being too old to participate in exercise
   D. A lack of time

4. Which is the **BEST** strategy for personal trainers to implement to enhance the likelihood that a client will continue working with them?
   A. Designing the program so the client can work out without having to think much about the exercises
   B. Motivating the client through extrinsic motivators to enhance self-efficacy
   C. Encouraging client ownership of the program to facilitate development of intrinsic motivation
   D. Creating an exercise coaching style based primarily on direction rather than education

5. A person who is confident that he or she can successfully participate regularly in an exercise program _____.
   A. Has good self-efficacy related to exercise
   B. Is in the contemplation stage of behavior change
   C. Has very strong self-esteem
   D. Is completely intrinsically motivated

6. Which of the following would be **MOST** likely to enhance program participation and goal attainment?
   A. Setting a series of progressively attainable short-term goals
   B. Helping clients keep a primary focus on never missing a session
   C. Setting many goals to ensure some type of program success
   D. Keeping clients focused on their primary long-term goals

7. A strong social support network can provide an individual with all of the following **EXCEPT** _____.
   A. Improved program adherence
   B. Extrinsic motivation
   C. Relapse-prevention support
   D. Intrinsic motivation

8. Which type of exercise program would be expected to have the **GREATEST** drop-out rate?
   A. Small-group personal training
   B. Vigorous-intensity exercise program
   C. Home-based personal training
   D. Moderate-intensity exercise program

9. Which of the following is generally considered to be unrelated to adherence levels in supervised exercise settings?
   A. Education
   B. Age
   C. Income
   D. Gender

10. After completing one year of personal training, Gina said that she had learned a great deal from you and wanted to try to continue her program on her own. During the six months that have followed, you have noticed Gina routinely coming into the gym to exercise for one or two hours on four or five days of the week. When you talk with her about it, she says that she "loves coming into the gym and feels great after her workouts." This statement reflects Gina's strong

    _____.

    A. Extrinsic motivation
    B. Self-esteem
    C. Intrinsic motivation
    D. Program design skills

Show What You Know

I. You have a new client, Joe Kammle, who needs to lose weight for medical reasons but is unwilling to stop smoking, and thus finds physical activity particularly challenging. After a month of working hard, Joe is beginning to lose interest in exercising. Describe the steps you can take to help maintain Joe's healthy exercise behavior. _____

   _____

   _____

   _____

   _____

II. Explain when it may be necessary to emphasize the short-term benefits of physical activity to improve a client's level of motivation. _____

   _____

   _____

   _____

   _____

Practice What You Know

Interview four or five active personal trainers to find out how they deal with burnout and how they help motivate clients.

CHAPTER 3

Communication and Teaching Techniques

Summary Review

Successful personal trainers consistently demonstrate excellent communication and teaching techniques. Positive and productive working relationships between clients and trainers are based on good communication.

Stages of the Client–Trainer Relationship

The early phase of the client–trainer relationship consists of the following four stages, each requiring somewhat different communication skills on the part of the personal trainer:

- Rapport
  - ✓ Making good first impressions
  - ✓ Utilizing verbal communication
  - ✓ Utilizing nonverbal communication
    - o Voice quality
    - o Eye contact
    - o Facial expressions
    - o Hand gestures
    - o Body position
  - ✓ Assessing and understanding personality styles
- Investigation stage
  - ✓ Gathering information
  - ✓ Demonstrating effective listening
    - o Encouraging
    - o Paraphrasing
    - o Questioning
    - o Reflecting
    - o Summarizing
  - ✓ Responding to difficult disclosures
- Planning stage
  - ✓ Setting goals
    - o Specific
    - o Measurable
    - o Attainable
    - o Relevant
    - o Time-bound
  - ✓ Generating and discussing alternatives
  - ✓ Formulating a plan
  - ✓ Evaluating the exercise program
  - ✓ Using motivational interviewing techniques
- Action stage
  - ✓ Setting up self-monitoring systems
  - ✓ Individualizing teaching techniques
  - ✓ Using the "tell, show, do" approach
  - ✓ Providing feedback
  - ✓ Using effective modeling
  - ✓ Creating behavior contracts

Strategies for Effective Communication

Effective communication grows out of personal trainers' knowledge and understanding of, and attitudes toward, their clients.

Cultural Competence Increases Empathy and Rapport

Personal trainers who work with people from different backgrounds can develop cultural competence by taking time to learn about clients' beliefs, attitudes, and lifestyles.

Difficult Clients May Require More Effort

Building rapport with difficult clients may involve more time spent doing the following activities:

- Behaving professionally
- Asking probing questions
- Taking time to understand clients

Empathy and Rapport Enhance Adherence

The time spent establishing a good working relationship enhances adherence to behavior-change programs.

Professional Boundaries Enhance the Effectiveness of Personal Trainers

The professional effectiveness of personal trainers is undermined when they become too personally involved with their clients.

Stages of Learning and Their Application to the Client–Trainer Relationship

A common model of motor learning divides the process into the following three stages:

- Cognitive stage
- Associative stage
- Autonomous stage

How to Incorporate Effective Communication and Teaching Techniques Into Daily Interactions With Clients

Personal trainers can continue to build productive relationships with clients by using the following techniques:

- Periodically reinforcing credentials
- Preparing for each session by cultivating a mindful focus
- Asking clients for feedback about performance
- Using electronic communication channels with discretion
- Making training fun for clients

Getting Started

This chapter describes the various stages of the client–trainer relationship, as well as methods of establishing and maintaining a relationship with clients that will enable them to successfully undergo positive lifestyle changes. After completing this chapter, you will have a better understanding of:

- The stages of the client–trainer relationship: rapport, investigation, planning, and action
- Strategies for effective communication
- How cultural competence increases both empathy and rapport, and how they, in turn, enhance adherence
- The stages of learning and their application to the client–trainer relationship
- How to incorporate effective communication and teaching techniques into daily interactions with clients

Reading Assignment

Read Chapter 3 of the *ACE Personal Trainer Manual,* 4th edition, paying special attention to the boldface terms in the chapter. After you have read the chapter, define those terms on a separate piece of paper.

Expand Your Knowledge

I.   List the common markers of positive and negative experiences with healthcare providers, allied health professionals, and health and fitness professionals.

    a. Positive _____

    _____

    _____

    _____

    _____

    _____

    _____

    b. Negative _____

    _____

    _____

    _____

    _____

    _____

    _____

II. Fill in the blanks.

    a. If someone's words and body language do not match, people generally trust _____ over _____.

    b. A _____ goal is something a client does, such as walk 2 miles a certain number of times; a _____ goal is something achieved, like weight loss or a resistance lifted on a resistance machine. _____ goals work better, because they are more predictable and controllable.

    c. Behavior-change contracts offer _____ motivation for exercise, which may be helpful for clients getting started.

    d. _____ can be defined as the ability to communicate and work effectively with people from different cultures.

III. List five key components of nonverbal communication.

a. _____

b. _____

c. _____

d. _____

e. _____

IV. Complete the following figure by writing in the four personality styles.

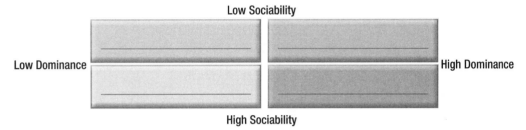

V. Match the four personality styles to the appropriate descriptions.

1. More affective and less cognitive; amiable, warm, trusting, and honest; avoid unnecessary risks and non-confrontational; team- and ask-oriented, gathering information to reach consensus over conflict

   a. _____ Deliberators

   b. _____ Directors

2. More affective and less cognitive; overly ambitious, risk-driven, and favor incentives and rewards; impulsive and lack discipline to complete projects; dominant, tell-oriented visionaries who thrive on excitement, challenge, and creativity

   c. _____ Collaborators

   d. _____ Expressors

3. More cognitive and less affective; methodical, favoring logic, objectivity, analysis, and accuracy; problem-solvers, working alone or in small groups; appear distant and uninterested in social interaction

4. More cognitive and less affective; action-oriented, competitive, take-charge, dominant personality; poor listeners, as they proactively think ahead to problem solving; emotionally reserved, valuing time over relationships

VI. Match the following sample responses with the corresponding listening skills.

a. ____ "I know what you mean."

b. ____ "It sounds like you have been most successful in the past when working out with a coworker."

c. ____ "You said that you stopped going to your yoga class last winter. What made you stop?"

d. ____ "You were able to maintain a weight of 180 pounds for quite a while. That seems like a realistic goal weight for you."

e. ____ "So it sounds like you've been walking about 2 miles twice each week in addition to doing a few hours of yard work each weekend…"

> 1. Paraphrasing
> 2. Reflecting
> 3. Questioning
> 4. Summarizing
> 5. Encouraging

VII. List eight tips for setting health and fitness goals that motivate clients for long-term adherence.

a. _____

_____

b. _____

_____

c. _____

_____

d. _____

_____

e. _____

_____

f. _____

_____

g. _____

_____

h. _____

_____

VIII. Explain how self-monitoring systems can support behavior change, including exercise program adherence._____

_____

_____

_____

_____

_____

_____

IX. Which of the following is an example of correctly phrased feedback? _____

    a. "Don't hold your breath as the exercise gets harder. Your breathing and timing were just right on the first four lifts. You'll find the work easier now that you are learning how to breathe correctly."

    b. "Your breathing and timing were just right on the first four lifts. Remember to keep breathing, even as the exercise starts to feel harder. You'll find the work easier now that you are learning how to breathe correctly."

    c. "Great job! You'll find the work easier now that you are learning how to breathe correctly. But remember to keep breathing, even as the exercise starts to feel harder."

X. Match the three stages of learning to the appropriate movement descriptions.

    1. Movements are uncoordinated and jerky.

    2. Movements are being performed effectively and naturally.

    3. Basic movements are mastered, but refinement is necessary.

    a. _____ Cognitive stage of learning

    b. _____ Associative stage of learning

    c. _____ Autonomous stage of learning

ACE Personal Trainer Master the Manual

Multiple-choice Questions

1. Which of the following would help a trainer develop rapport with a client during the initial session?
   A. Looking away from the client frequently to prevent staring while sitting with good posture and a slight forward lean
   B. Speaking in a soft, friendly voice while leaning against the chair armrest with forearms crossed calmly
   C. Direct, friendly eye contact while always maintaining a smile and enthusiasm throughout the session
   D. Speaking in a firm voice with confidence, using fluid hand gestures while speaking and quiet hands while listening

2. Providing a more detailed description of the process by which resistance training helps to preserve bone density would be **MOST** effective with which personality style?
   A. Deliberator
   B. Director
   C. Collaborator
   D. Expressor

3. Implementing a system of rewards for each goal reached would be **MOST** effective with which personality style?
   A. Deliberator
   B. Director
   C. Collaborator
   D. Expressor

4. Active listening allows personal trainers to do which of the following effectively?
   A. Formulate responses and counterpoints to the client's beliefs and concerns
   B. Plan out the client's initial exercise program while expressing genuineness
   C. Gain a better understanding of the client to facilitate rapport and program design
   D. Record detailed notes about the client's exercise history and preferences

5. A client you have been working with for several months tells you that she believes her husband may be having an affair. Which response would be **MOST** appropriate?
   A. "I'm so sorry. I can't imagine how difficult that must be for you."
   B. "Have you considered marriage counseling? Some of my clients have had great success with it."
   C. "I can't believe he would do something like that! How did you find out?"
   D. "I'm so sorry. One of my clients is a counselor. Would you like to talk with him?"

6. Which of the following is a SMART goal?
   A. "I will improve my cholesterol and blood pressure through better eating and exercise."
   B. "I will run 4 days per week, gradually progressing my run time from 10 to 40 minutes, to prepare for a 5K in four months."
   C. "I will lose 20 lb (9 kg) for my trip to Hawaii in 2 months by exercising seven days a week to maximize results."
   D. "I will try a new group exercise class each week to avoid boredom."

7. What would be **MOST** effective in helping a client to develop program adherence?
   A. Providing the client with regular feedback about exercise form
   B. Having the client self-monitor by keeping an exercise journal
   C. Implementing a reward system for client goal attainment
   D. Conducting fitness assessments every other week to measure progress

8. What is the **MOST** effective way to teach a new exercise to a client?
   A. Show the client how to do the exercise, then have the client perform the exercise while mirroring to provide an example of good form
   B. Tell the client what the exercise is, demonstrate the exercise, and have the client perform the exercise while providing feedback
   C. Use photos of the exercise while explaining it to the client, and then have the client perform the exercise while providing feedback
   D. Have the client perform the exercise while providing verbal instructions to coach him or her through it with proper form

9. You are working with a client who is beginning to perform basic bodyweight squats with fairly decent form. She is now ready for more specific feedback to help her refine her squatting technique. In which stage of motor learning would she be classified for this exercise skill?
   A. Associative
   B. Cognitive
   C. Autonomous
   D. Independent

10. Which of the following strategies should be **AVOIDED** when a personal trainer is modeling the healthful lifestyle that he or she is trying to get clients to adopt?
    A. Promoting the notion that regular exercise is important and worth the cost
    B. Giving clients confidence that it can be done and they can reach their goals
    C. Providing "negative" reasons for regular exercise such as losing weight
    D. Displaying the attitude that physical activity can feel good and reduce stress

Practice What You Know

I. Complete the survey presented in Figure 3-3 to describe your own personality. Then, have three friends or colleagues complete the same survey describing you and compare the results. Do they see you in the same way you see yourself?

II. Interview a sedentary friend or family member using the motivational interviewing techniques presented in this chapter.

CHAPTER 4

Basics of Behavior Change and Health Psychology

Summary Review

It is critical that personal trainers understand the psychological and social components of behavior-change practices to help each client adopt and maintain an active lifestyle.

Behavioral Theory Models

Over the years, numerous explanations have been developed regarding the factors affecting health behaviors. Each of the following models has relevance for personal trainers.

Health Belief Model

- Perceived seriousness of the health problem
- Perceived susceptibility to the health problem
- Cues to action
- Self-efficacy
- Past performance experience
- Vicarious experience
- Verbal persuasion
- Physiological state appraisals
- Emotional state and mood appraisals
- Imaginal experiences

Transtheoretical Model of Behavioral Change

- Stages of change
  - ✓ Precontemplation
  - ✓ Contemplation
  - ✓ Preparation
  - ✓ Action
  - ✓ Maintenance
- Processes of change
- Self-efficacy
- Decisional balance
- Relapse

Operant Conditioning

- Antecedents
  - ✓ Stimulus control
- Consequences
  - ✓ Positive reinforcement
  - ✓ Negative reinforcement
  - ✓ Extinction
  - ✓ Punishment
- Shaping

Observational Learning

All people are influenced to some degree by the behaviors of people around them at home, at work, and in social environments. Trainers should encourage interactions with other people who are also physically active.

Cognitions and Behavior

Personal trainers should understand what their clients think about exercise and physical activity and lapses in program participation.

Behavior-change Strategies

Personal trainers can use the following behavior-change strategies as tools to enhance the likelihood that clients will successfully adopt and maintain a physical-activity program:

- Stimulus control
- Written agreements and behavioral contracting
- Cognitive behavioral techniques
  - ✓ Goal setting
  - ✓ Feedback
  - ✓ Decision making
  - ✓ Self-monitoring

Implementing Basic Behavior-change and Health-psychology Strategies

Successful personal trainers are able to use communication to gain a better understanding about each client. All information that is gathered through effective communication and observation should be used in program design and implementation.

Getting Started

This chapter addresses the analysis of health behaviors and theories of behavior change, with special attention given to those related to physical activity and exercise. After completing this chapter, you will have a better understanding of:

- Behavioral theory models, including the health belief model, self-efficacy, and the transtheoretical model of behavioral change
- Principles of behavior change, including operant conditioning and shaping
- How stimulus control can influence behavior change
- The proper and effective use of written agreements and behavioral contracts

Reading Assignment

Read Chapter 4 of the *ACE Personal Trainer Manual,* 4th edition, paying special attention to the boldface terms in the chapter. After you have read the chapter, define those terms on a separate piece of paper.

ACE Personal Trainer Master the Manual

Expand Your Knowledge

I. Match the principles of behavior change with the appropriate definitions.

1. Stimuli that precede a behavior

2. Stimuli that follow a behavior

3. A series of behavioral connections

4. Reinforcements to gradually achieve a target behavior

5. Thoughts, which can either motivate or demotivate

a. _____ Shaping

b. _____ Cognitions

c. _____ Antecedents

d. _____ Consequences

e. _____ Behavior chains

II. Explain the major differences between the following terms.

a. Maintenance and relapse _____

_____

_____

b. Antecedents and consequences _____

_____

_____

c. Precontemplation and preparation _____

_____

_____

d. Shaping and observational learning _____

_____

_____

e. Extinction and punishment _____

_____

_____

III. Briefly define the health belief model as it relates to health-related behaviors. _____

_____

_____

_____

_____

_____

IV. Fill in the blanks.

    a. Health psychology took the traditional biomedical model and added the _____ to the equation, resulting in a broader picture of the correlates of health and illness.

    b. _____ are events, either bodily or environmental, that motivate people to make a change.

    c. The assessment of _____ is an ongoing part of the client–trainer relationship and should not be thought of as a one-time measurement.

    d. The second component of the transtheoretical model of behavioral change is likely the most important for personal trainers to understand, as it entails the _____ that people use to get from one stage to the next.

    e. _____ is the process by which behaviors are influenced by their consequences.

V. List the six sources of self-efficacy information that personal trainers should explore with their clients.

    a. _____

    b. _____

    c. _____

    d. _____

    e. _____

    f. _____

VI. Match the five stages of change with the corresponding client descriptions.

    1. An individual who has a health-club membership and visits sporadically, but not consistently enough to maintain a well-rounded program

    2. An individual who has been exercising regularly for nine months, including two days per week with a personal trainer

    3. An individual who has been exercising regularly for four months, including three yoga sessions per week

    4. An individual who does not exercise and does not see the value in physical activity

    5. An individual who does not exercise, but has talked to his or her doctor about the implications of physical inactivity

    a. _____ Precontemplation

    b. _____ Contemplation

    c. _____ Preparation

    d. _____ Action

    e. _____ Maintenance

VII. Match the stage of change to the following descriptions by marking each as a characteristic of individuals in the precontemplation (PC) stage, contemplation (C) stage, preparation (P) stage, action (A) stage, or maintenance (M) stage. Note that some descriptions may be appropriate for multiple stages.

a. _____ Perceive more cons related to being regularly active than pros

b. _____ Perceive more pros related to being regularly active than cons

c. _____ Are prone to relapse

d. _____ Have as a primary goal to initiate regular physical-activity participation

e. _____ Have as a primary goal to get involved in some type of activity

VIII. Briefly describe the following behavior-change strategies and provide examples of each.

a. Stimulus control _____

_____

_____

_____

_____

b. Written agreements and behavior contracts _____

_____

_____

_____

_____

_____

c. Cognitive behavioral techniques _____

_____

_____

_____

_____

_____

Multiple-choice Questions

1. During your initial interview with a new client, you learn that his motivation to sign up for personal-training sessions was based on a recent medical exam during which his physician informed him that he was prehypertensive (BP = 137/88 mmHg) and had dyslipidemia (total serum cholesterol = 227 mg/dL), and a family history of cardiovascular disease. Based on this information, his motivation to exercise is **MOST** likely associated with which of the following?
   A. Health belief model
   B. Transtheoretical model
   C. Operant conditioning
   D. Cognitive behavioral techniques

2. While on an airplane, you are talking with the man next to you and tell him that you are a personal trainer. This opens up a conversation during which the man asks you a number of questions about things he has read recently regarding exercise, nutrition, and health. He says that he does not currently exercise, but he has been thinking about joining a gym and asks you for recommendations. Based on this information, in what stage of behavior change would he be categorized?
   A. Precontemplation
   B. Contemplation
   C. Preparation
   D. Action

3. What is the **MOST** influential source of self-efficacy information related to exercise?
   A. Persuasive verbal feedback
   B. Emotional state and mood
   C. Past exercise performance
   D. Vicarious exercise experiences

4. A new client tells you that she used to participate in local 10K and half-marathon running events before having twins. Although she had wanted to continue running, she has not been active since her children were born two years ago. Now that they are in daycare three days per week, she has begun walking a bit and wants to begin running, with an eventual goal of completing her first marathon. Based on this information, what stages of change has she gone through from pre-pregnancy to meeting with you today?
   A. Action → Precontemplation → Action
   B. Maintenance → Contemplation → Action
   C. Action → Maintenance → Preparation
   D. Maintenance → Contemplation → Preparation

5. Which of the following is an example of an effective cognitive behavioral technique that a personal trainer can implement to improve client exercise adherence?
   A. Revisiting client goals only during reassessments so they reflect greater progress
   B. Making primary decisions regarding each client's program so that they can focus on the exercises
   C. Helping clients move from primarily external feedback to primarily internal feedback
   D. Recording progress so clients can focus on the exercises without having to monitor their own progress

6. In the process of operant conditioning, which of the following consequences would be **BEST** for a personal trainer to use to ensure that a desired client behavior will reoccur in the future?
   A. Punishment
   B. Positive reinforcement
   C. Extinction of a positive stimulus
   D. Negative reinforcement

7. Using reinforcement to help a client progress from doing a quarter lunge to performing a full lunge and then eventually adding resistance is an example of which process?
   A. Shaping
   B. Operant conditioning
   C. Cognitions and behavior
   D. Observational learning

8. Sending personal-training appointment reminder emails to clients would be an example of which behavior-change strategy?
   A. Cognitions and behavior
   B. Stimulus control
   C. Cognitive behavioral techniques
   D. Shaping

9. A new personal-training client tells you that she has little experience with exercise, but has signed up for eight weeks of personal training because she is ready to get fit and lose weight. Based on this information, what would be the **MOST** effective way to help her to become regularly active and work toward her goals?
   A. Design a challenging program so she can experience the positive benefits of exercise
   B. Inform her about different types of exercise and invite her to your group strength class
   C. Provide her with initial positive exercise experiences and help her focus on consistency
   D. Educate her about the risks of being inactive and commend her on her new commitment

10. Which of the following strategies should a personal trainer **AVOID** when trying to promote program ownership on the part of the client?
    A. Having clients journal their thoughts, experiences, and emotions related to the program
    B. Giving clients the information needed to determine the outcome of their programs
    C. Helping clients to reinforce their own behaviors through internal encouragement
    D. Providing clients with increasing amounts of external feedback as the program progresses

Practice What You Know

Review the Examples of the Processes of Change in the TTM on page 71 and initiate conversations with friends and family members at various points on the stages-of-change continuum. After each conversation, assess your performance with that "client" and work on ways to become more persuasive and effective.

CHAPTER 5

Introduction to the ACE Integrated Fitness Training™ Model

Summary Review

A personal trainer should be familiar with the following concepts related to providing services as a fitness professional:
- Traditional physiological training parameters versus new physiological training parameters
- General exercise recommendations for healthy adults

Health—Fitness—Performance Continuum

A personal trainer should understand the health—fitness—performance continuum and how it relates to individual client exercise programming.

Introduction to the ACE Integrated Fitness Training Model

ACE-certified Personal Trainers should understand the following terms and concepts related to the ACE Integrated Fitness Training (ACE IFT™) Model and how each one influences the development, implementation, and/or progression of a client's exercise program:
- Assessment sequencing for the general client
- ACE IFT Model phases and the health—fitness—performance continuum
- Rapport
- Behavioral strategies
- Training components and phases

Functional Movement and Resistance Training

Because functional movement and resistance training are integral parts of the ACE IFT Model, an ACE-certified Personal Trainer should understand how these modalities are represented in the following content areas:
- Phase 1: Stability and mobility training
  - ✓ Basic assessments (i.e., posture, balance, movement, range of motion)
- Phase 2: Movement training
  - ✓ Five primary movements of exercise
- Phase 3: Load training
  - ✓ Periodization (linear versus undulating)
- Phase 4: Performance training
  - ✓ Power, speed, agility, and quickness

Cardiorespiratory Training

Because cardiorespiratory training is an integral part of the ACE IFT Model, an ACE-certified Personal Trainer should understand how this mode of exercise is represented in the following content areas:

- Phase 1: Aerobic-base training
  - ✓ First ventilatory threshold (VT1)
- Phase 2: Aerobic-efficiency training
  - ✓ Second ventilatory threshold (VT2)
  - ✓ Three-zone cardiorespiratory training model
- Phase 3: Anaerobic-endurance training
- Phase 4: Anaerobic-power training

Special Population Clientele

ACE-certified Personal Trainers working with special-population clients should understand how to utilize the integrated training process provided in the ACE IFT Model, being sure to adjust exercise selection, intensity, sets, repetitions, and duration to fit the special needs of each client.

Getting Started

This chapter introduces the ACE IFT Model. After completing this chapter, you will have a better understanding of:

- The health—fitness—performance continuum
- How rapport and behavioral strategies fit within this training model
- The training components and phases of the model, including functional movement and resistance training and cardiorespiratory training

Reading Assignment

Read Chapter 5 of the *ACE Personal Trainer Manual,* 4th edition, paying special attention to the boldface terms in the chapter. After you have read the chapter, define those terms on a separate piece of paper.

Expand Your Knowledge

I.   List the 12 new physiological training parameters addressed in the ACE IFT Model.

a. _____

b. _____

c. _____

d. _____

e. _____

f. _____

g. _____

h. _____

i. _____

j. _____

k. _____

l. _____

II. Fill in the blanks.

a. The *2008 Physical Activity Guidelines for Americans* suggest that adults should participate in structured physical activity at a moderate intensity for at least _____ per week or a vigorous intensity for at least _____ per week to experience the health benefits of exercise.

b. The first goal of the ACE IFT Model is exercise for _____.

c. The foundation of the ACE IFT Model is build upon _____.

d. At the core of human movement is _____.

III. Give two reasons why the collection of health-history information is such a critical process early in the client–trainer relationship.

a. _____

b. _____

IV. List the two principal training components of the ACE IFT Model.

a. _____

b. _____

V.   Complete the following table by listing the training focus of each phase of the ACE IFT Model.

Training Component	Phase 1	Phase 2	Phase 3	Phase 4
Functional Movement & Resistance Training				
Cardiorespiratory Training				

VI. Describe the primary focus of each of the four training phases of the ACE IFT Model.

    a. Phase 1 _____

    _____

    _____

    b. Phase 2 _____

    _____

    _____

    c. Phase 3 _____

    _____

    _____

    d. Phase 4 _____

    _____

    _____

VII. How might a complete battery of initial assessments be detrimental to early program

    success for an out-of-shape client? _____

    _____

    _____

    _____

    _____

VIII. List three reasons why clients will generally experience more stable positive moods after
two to four weeks of regular physical activity.

    a. _____

    _____

    b. _____

    _____

    c. _____

    _____

IX. Match each phase of the functional movement and resistance training component to the appropriate descriptions.

1. Any resistance training performed should include exercises that build muscular endurance and promote mobility

2. Exercises use primarily bodyweight and body-segment weight as resistance

a. _____ Stability and mobility training

b. _____ Movement training

c. _____ Load training

d. _____ Performance training

3. External force is introduced, emphasizing muscle force production

4. Speed and agility are addressed

5. Assessments should focus on posture, balance, movement, and range of motion at specific joints

6. Assessments of muscular strength and endurance are introduced to facilitate program design and quantify progress

7. Exercises should emphasize supported surfaces that offer stability against gravity

8. Incorporates power training into the program

9. Training focuses on the five primary movements of exercise

10. Periodization models are often introduced

11. Whole-body movement patterns that utilize gravity as the source of external resistance are emphasized

12. Clients must have prerequisite stability, mobility, strength, and skills before entering this phase of training

X. Match each phase of the cardiorespiratory training component to the appropriate descriptions.

1. Exercise should be performed at an RPE of 5 (0 to 10 scale)

2. Exercise intensity can exceed an RPE of 9 (0 to 10 scale)

a. _____ Aerobic-base training

b. _____ Aerobic-efficiency training

c. _____ Anaerobic-endurance training

d. _____ Anaerobic-power training

3. Exercise should be performed at steady-state intensities in the low-to-moderate range

4. Exercise should be performed at an RPE of 3 to 4 (0 to 10 scale)

5. No assessments are recommended

6. A submaximal talk test can be used to determine the client's heart rate at the first ventilatory threshold (VT1)

7. The VT2 threshold test can be performed

8. The three-zone training model is introduced

9. One goal is to improve the client's ability to use fat as a fuel source

10. Exercise in this phase will increase the amount of sustained work an individual can perform at or near the second ventilatory threshold (VT2)

11. Short-duration, high-intensity intervals are performed

12. Many clients will never reach this phase of training

Multiple-choice Questions

1. What foundational element is the ACE IFT Model built upon?
   A. Health improvement
   B. Functional fitness
   C. Developing rapport
   D. Cardiorespiratory fitness

2. What assessments are essential according to the ACE IFT Model and should be completed prior to a client beginning an exercise program?
   A. Assessing posture, functional movement, and muscular strength and endurance
   B. Collecting health-history data to identify contraindications for exercise and the need for referral
   C. Assessing cardiorespiratory fitness using the submaximal talk test to determine HR at VT1
   D. Measuring blood pressure, resting heart rate, body composition, and waist-to-hip ratio

3. Which of the following is **MOST** likely to create a barrier to fitness-related behavior change for some clients?
   A. Identifying a client's readiness to change behavior
   B. Creating early positive exercise experiences
   C. Implementing strategies for working with clients based on their personality styles
   D. Conducting initial comprehensive assessments of fitness and body composition

4. What are the five primary movements that are the focus of the movement-training phase?
   A. Squatting, lunging, swinging, throwing, and arching movements
   B. Jumping, hopping, pushing, pulling, and arching movements
   C. Squatting, lunging, pushing, pulling, and rotational movements
   D. Jumping, hopping, swinging, throwing, and rotational movements

5. In what phase of the functional movement and resistance training component of the ACE IFT Model would a person be categorized if he has lumbar lordosis, limited range of motion in the hips and shoulders, and performs resistance-training workouts four days per week?
   A. Phase 1: Stability and mobility training
   B. Phase 2: Movement training
   C. Phase 3: Load training
   D. Phase 4: Performance training

6. Strength training, body building, and training for muscular endurance all fall under which functional movement and resistance training phase of the ACE IFT Model?
   A. Phase 1: Stability and mobility training
   B. Phase 2: Movement training
   C. Phase 3: Load training
   D. Phase 4: Performance training

7. Performance training includes speed, agility, quickness, and reactivity drills that would be **MOST** appropriate for which of the following clients?
    A. 45-year-old male, competitive tennis player
    B. 33-year-old female, marathon runner
    C. 27-year-old male, body builder
    D. 52-year-old female, competitive golfer

8. A regular group exercise participant with no competitive goals would be classified in which phase of the cardiorespiratory training component of the ACE IFT Model?
    A. Phase 1: Aerobic-base training
    B. Phase 2: Aerobic-efficiency training
    C. Phase 3: Anaerobic-endurance training
    D. Phase 4: Anaerobic-power training

9. Personal trainers can use the talk test as an upper limit for exercise intensity to determine if a client is exercising below which of the following cardiorespiratory markers?
    A. $\dot{V}O_2max$
    B. The second ventilatory threshold (VT2)
    C. Anaerobic threshold
    D. The first ventilatory threshold (VT1)

10. Cardiorespiratory exercise in zone 2 is performed at what intensity?
    A. Below VT1
    B. At or above VT1
    C. From VT1 to just below VT2
    D. At or above VT2

CHAPTER 6

Building Rapport and the Initial Investigation Stage

Summary Review

It is imperative for a personal trainer to make a strong and positive first impression. The following three attributes are essential for successful relationships:

- Empathy
- Warmth
- Genuineness

There are four essential stages in building client–trainer relationships:

- Rapport
- Investigation
- Planning
- Action

A personal trainer must be aware of the following factors that can affect communication between the client and fitness professional:

- Environment
- Effective communication
- Empathy
- Interviewing techniques

Facilitating Change and Motivational Interviewing

A personal trainer should understand theoretical models of behavior change, such as the transtheoretical model of behavioral change, and have knowledge of motivational interviewing techniques for enhancing a client's intrinsic motivation to change.

The Health-risk Appraisal

A personal trainer must have a thorough understanding of the following concepts related to health-risk appraisal:

- The purposes of the pre-participation screen
- Whether the exercise program is self-directed or being conducted under the consultation and supervision of a qualified fitness professional
- The basis for, and importance of, performing a risk stratification prior to engaging in a physical-activity program
- The three basic steps for performing a risk stratification
- The signs and symptoms of coronary artery disease (CAD)
- Atherosclerotic cardiovascular disease risk factor thresholds for use with ACSM risk stratification

Evaluation Forms

A personal trainer should have an understanding of common evaluation forms for use with clients:
- PAR-Q
- CAD health-risk assessment
- Informed consent
- Agreement and release of liability
- Health-history questionnaire
- Exercise history and attitude questionnaire

Health Conditions That Affect Physical Activity

Personal trainers should have an understanding of how the following health conditions and medications affect physical activity:
- Cardiovascular disease
- Hypertension
- Respiratory problems
- Musculoskeletal problems
- Metabolic disorders
- Hernia
- Pregnancy
- Illness or infection
- Antihypertensive medication
- Bronchodilators
- Cold medications

Sequencing Assessments

The following concepts are related to the selection, timing, and sequencing of client assessments:
- The appropriateness of conducting assessments with clients
- Physiological influences on assessment
- Signs and symptoms that merit immediate test termination and referral to a more qualified healthcare professional
- Professionalism and the testing environment

Choosing the Right Assessments

A personal trainer should take into account the following factors when choosing health/fitness assessments for their clients:
- Goals of the assessment
- Physical limitations of the participant
- Testing environment
- Availability of equipment
- Age of the participant

Conducting Essential Cardiovascular Assessments

Personal trainers should have an understanding of the following assessments and the impact of the assessment results on a client's program design:
- Heart rate (exercise and resting)
- Blood pressure
- Exercise-induced feeling inventory

Ratings of Perceived Exertion

Knowledge of common trends relating to, and recommendations for use of, subjective scales of ratings of perceived exertion is essential for personal trainers.

Getting Started

This chapter covers the earliest stages of the client–trainer relationship. After completing this chapter, you will have a better understanding of:

- Facilitating change and motivational interviewing
- How to perform a health-risk appraisal and utilize common forms
- How various health conditions and medications affect the body's response to exercise
- How to choose and schedule assessments so that the process is appropriate for each client
- How to accurately measure clients' heart rate and blood pressure

Reading Assignment

Read Chapter 6 of the *ACE Personal Trainer Manual,* 4th edition, paying special attention to the boldface terms in the chapter. After you have read the chapter, define those terms on a separate piece of paper.

Expand Your Knowledge

I.   List and describe three attributes that are essential to successful relationships.

a. _____

_____

b. _____

_____

c. _____

_____

II. How is rapport-building different from the latter three stages of a successful client–trainer relationship? _____

_____

III. List the four stages of the client–trainer relationship and explain what each involves.

a. _____

_____

b. _____

_____

c. _____

_____

d. _____

_____

IV. What should be a personal trainer's first objective when meeting a prospective client?

_____

_____

V. What are three ways that a personal trainer can attend to the environment where he or she meets with a prospective or current client?

a. _____

_____

b. _____

_____

c. _____

_____

VI. Define the following types of listening.

a. Indifferent listening _____

_____

b. Selective listening _____

_____

c. Passive listening _____

_____

d. Active listening _____

_____

VII. Fill in the blanks.

a. _____ is a client-centered, directive method for enhancing intrinsic motivation to change by exploring and resolving ambivalence.

b. The transtheoretical model of behavioral change is also called the _____ model.

c. The _____ is a minimal, yet safe, pre-exercise screening measure for low-to-moderate, but not vigorous, exercise training.

d. If a client answers "yes" to _____ or more questions on the PAR-Q, he or she should be referred to a healthcare professional.

e. To stratify a client's risk for coronary artery disease, the trainer should add up the total number of risk factors for a client, subtracting one point for higher _____ if appropriate.

VIII. List the four purposes of the pre-participation health screening.

a. _____

_____

b. _____

_____

c. _____

_____

d. _____

_____

IX. List the three steps of the risk-stratification process in the proper order.

a. _____

b. _____

c. _____

X. Which of the following would qualify as positive risk factors for coronary artery disease?

a. _____ A man who is 47 years of age

b. _____ Participating in 45 minutes each day of moderate-intensity physical activity

c. _____ A woman with a waist circumference measurement of 86 cm

d. _____ BMI = 32 kg/m^2

e. _____ Systolic blood pressure = 140 mmHg

f. _____ An individual taking antihypertensive medication

g. _____ HDL cholesterol = 64 mg/dL

XI. Match each of the following evaluation forms with their proper descriptions.

1. This form does not necessarily protect the trainer from being sued for negligence.

2. When a client signs this form, he or she is acknowledging having been specifically informed about the risks associated with activity.

3. This form collects more detailed medical and health information beyond the coronary artery disease risk-factor screen.

a. _____ Informed consent form

b. _____ Agreement and release of liability waiver

c. _____ Health-history questionnaire

d. _____ Exercise history and attitude questionnaire

e. _____ Medical release

f. _____ Testing form

4. It is recommended that the trainer also verbally review the content of this form to promote understanding.

5. This form explains a client's physical-activity limitations and/or guidelines as outlined by his or her physician.

6. The information listed on this form is especially important when developing goals and designing exercise programs with a client, and when implementing strategies for improving motivation and adherence.

7. This form does not provide legal immunity.

8. This form represents the client's voluntary abandonment of the right to file a lawsuit.

9. This form includes a client's behavioral and adherence experience specific to physical activity.

10. The client should list any medications or supplements being taken on this form.

11. This form is used to record testing and measurement data during fitness assessments.

12. Deviation from the guidelines provided in this form must be approved by the client's personal physician.

XII. Fill in the blanks.

    a. If a person's resting blood pressure is already high, it may elevate to dangerous levels during exercise, increasing the likelihood of a _____.

    b. _____ is defined as difficult or labored breathing.

    c. The most common type of injury sustained by persons participating in physical activity is the _____.

    d. To avoid aggravating an existing injury, and to allow for healing to occur, trainers should modify the client's exercise program using a _____ strategy.

    e. Exercise, both as a means to regulate blood glucose and to facilitate fat loss, is an important part of the lifestyle of an individual with _____.

XIII. Antihypertensive medications primarily affect one of four different sites. Explain how this type of medication would affect each of the following.

    a. Heart _____

    b. Peripheral blood vessels _____

    c. Brain _____

    d. Kidneys _____

XIV. Match each type of medication with its description.

    1. Using ratings of perceived exertion is especially appropriate when working with a client taking this type of medication.

    2. Have no primary affect on heart rate, but will cause a decrease in blood pressure at rest and during exercise

    3. Have no primary affect on heart rate, but they can cause water and electrolyte imbalances, which may lead to dangerous cardiac arrhythmias

    4. Do not have a direct affect on the heart rate or blood pressure, but produce a drying effect in the upper airways and may cause drowsiness

    5. Act directly on the smooth muscles of the blood vessels to stimulate vasoconstriction

a. _____ Beta blockers
b. _____ Diuretics
c. _____ ACE inhibitors
d. _____ Decongestants
e. _____ Antihistamines

XV. List the eight signs or symptoms that personal trainers can identify that merit immediate test termination and referral to a more qualified health professional.

a. _____

_____

b. _____

_____

c. _____

_____

d. _____

_____

e. _____

_____

f. _____

_____

g. _____

_____

h. _____

_____

XVI. List five important considerations when choosing assessments for a client.

a. _____

b. _____

c. _____

d. _____

e. _____

Multiple-choice Questions

1. What is the name of the essential attribute of successful relationships that is described as "the ability to respect another person regardless of his or her uniqueness?"
   A. Empathy
   B. Warmth
   C. Genuineness
   D. Honesty

2. "When do you experience your low-back soreness?" is an example of what type of interviewing technique?
   A. Reflecting
   B. Confronting
   C. Informing
   D. Probing

USE THE FOLLOWING CLIENT INFORMATION TO ANSWER QUESTIONS 3–5:

Gender:	Male
Age:	47 years
Family history:	Mother has hypertension; father had coronary bypass surgery at age 59
Smoking:	Quit smoking 20 years ago
Current exercise:	Walks dog 1–2 times per day for 10 minutes per walk
BMI:	29 kg/m²
Blood pressure:	132/86 mmHg
Total serum cholesterol:	216 mg/dL
LDL cholesterol:	138 mg/dL
HDL cholesterol:	48 mg/dL
Fasting plasma glucose:	94 mg/dL
Goals:	Lose 20 lb (9 kg); increase muscle strength and cardiorespiratory fitness

3. What is this client's "total score" for atherosclerotic cardiovascular disease using the ACSM risk factor thresholds?
   A. +1
   B. +2
   C. +3
   D. +4

4. According to the ACSM risk stratification, what is this client's level of risk?
   A. Low risk
   B. Moderate risk
   C. High risk
   D. Very high risk

5. What are the recommendations regarding exercise testing based on this client's risk stratification?
   A. Trainer can perform submaximal fitness testing without a physician's supervision
   B. Trainer can perform both submaximal and maximal fitness testing without a physician's supervision
   C. A physician should be present for all submaximal and maximal fitness testing
   D. A medical exam and graded exercise test are required prior to beginning an exercise program

USE THE FOLLOWING CLIENT INFORMATION TO ANSWER QUESTIONS 6–7:

Gender:	Female
Age:	39 years
Family history:	Father has type 1 diabetes; Mother just diagnosed with type 2 diabetes
Smoking:	Never smoked
Current exercise:	Swims 3–4 days per week for 30–45 minutes
BMI:	31 kg/m²
Blood pressure:	128/82 mmHg
Total serum cholesterol:	224 mg/dL
LDL cholesterol:	122 mg/dL
HDL cholesterol:	64 mg/dL
Fasting plasma glucose:	95 mg/dL
Goals:	Lose 30 lb (13.5 kg); enhance exercise program and improve diet to prevent diabetes

6. What is this client's "total score" for atherosclerotic cardiovascular disease using the ACSM risk factor thresholds?
   A. 0
   B. +1
   C. +2
   D. +3

7. What are the recommendations regarding the intensity of the cardiorespiratory exercise program and the need for a medical examination and graded exercise test based on this client's risk stratification?
   A. The trainer can design a program with the client performing moderate-intensity exercise, but a medical exam and exercise test would be recommended prior to vigorous-intensity exercise
   B. The trainer can design a program with the client performing moderate- or vigorous-intensity exercise without the client needing a medical exam or exercise test
   C. An exercise test is recommended prior to moderate-intensity exercise, and a medical exam and exercise test are recommended prior to vigorous-intensity exercise
   D. A medical exam and graded exercise test are required prior to beginning an exercise program

8. Your new client is a 57-year-old woman who plays golf, tennis, and squash avidly. Her health-risk appraisal reveals only one positive risk factor (age) and that she has a heart murmur. According to the ACSM risk stratification, what is this client's level of risk?
   A. Low risk
   B. Moderate risk
   C. High risk
   D. Very high risk

9. Which evaluation form does a client sign to acknowledge that he or she has been educated about, and understands, the risks associated with being active?
   A. Agreement and release of liability waiver
   B. Medical release
   C. Exercise history and attitude questionnaire
   D. Informed consent

10. A personal trainer could design an exercise program without requiring a physician's release prior to participation for which of the following?
    A. 42-year-old female client who has lumbar lordosis
    B. 54-year-old male client who has an abdominal hernia
    C. 61-year-old female client who takes a calcium channel blocker
    D. 35-year-old male client who has asthma

Practice What You Know

I. Complete the forms presented in Figures 6-5, 6-6, and 6-7 with friends or family members. Use the information to determine if each individual is a suitable candidate for personal training and, if so, outline a plan for how you would proceed.

II. Review the procedures for measuring heart rate and blood pressure and practice with friends, family members, or clients.

III. Fill out the exercise-induced feeling inventory one day at work and then periodically after workouts. Chart any changes in your own feelings and think about how to use this type of information when training clients.

Functional Assessments: Posture, Movement, Core, Balance, and Flexibility

Summary Review

One primary objective of all training programs should be to improve functionality to help clients enhance their abilities to perform activities of daily living (ADL). Since posture is the foundation for all movement, personal trainers should incorporate assessments to evaluate static posture. Trainers should also incorporate movement screens to evaluate movement compensations in their clients.

Static Postural Assessment

A static postural assessment may offer valuable insight into:
- Muscle imbalance at a joint and the working relationships of muscles around a joint
- Altered neural action of the muscles moving and controlling the joint

Muscle imbalance and postural deviations can be attributed to many factors that are both correctible and non-correctible, including the following:
- Correctible factors
  ✓ Repetitive movements
  ✓ Awkward positions and movements
  ✓ Side dominance
  ✓ Lack of joint stability
  ✓ Lack of joint mobility
  ✓ Imbalanced strength-training programs
- Non-correctible factors
  ✓ Congenital conditions
  ✓ Some pathologies
  ✓ Structural deviations
  ✓ Certain types of trauma

Personal trainers should be familiar with the protocols for the assessment of, and the practical implications of, the following five common postural deviations:
- Deviation 1: Ankle pronation/supination and the effect on tibial and femoral rotation
- Deviation 2: Hip adduction
- Deviation 3: Hip tilting (anterior or posterior)
- Deviation 4: Shoulder position and the thoracic spine
- Deviation 5: Head position

Movement Screens

Movement can essentially be broken down and described by five primary movements that people perform during many daily activities:
- Bending/raising and lifting/lowering movements
- Single-leg movements

- Pushing movements and resultant movement
- Pulling movements and resultant movement
- Rotational movements

Personal trainers should be familiar with the protocols for the following common movement screens, as well as the practical implications for clients who have challenges with these screens:

- Clearing tests
  - ✓ Cervical spine
  - ✓ Shoulder impingement
  - ✓ Low back
- Bend and lift screen
- Hurdle step screen
- Shoulder push stabilization screen
- Shoulder pull stabilization screen
- Thoracic spine mobility screen

Flexibility and Muscle-length Testing

Personal trainers should be familiar with the protocols for the following common flexibility and muscle-length tests, as well as the practical implications for clients who have challenges with these tests:

- Thomas test for hip flexion/quadriceps length
- Passive straight-leg (PSL) raise

Shoulder Mobility

Personal trainers should be familiar with the protocols for the following common shoulder mobility tests, as well as the practical implications for clients who have challenges with these tests:

- Shoulder flexion and extension
- Internal and external rotation of the humerus at the shoulder
- Apley's scratch test for shoulder mobility

Balance and the Core

Personal trainers should be familiar with the protocols for the following common balance and core function tests, as well as the practical implications for clients who have challenges with these tests:

- Sharpened Romberg test
- Stork-stand balance test
- Core function: Blood pressure cuff test

Getting Started

This chapter explains the importance of various functional assessments and outlines how to properly perform each. After completing this chapter, you will have a better understanding of: How to set up a plumb line for use in postural assessments

- The five key postural deviations
- How to conduct various movement screens, including clearing tests
- How to conduct flexibility and muscle-length testing
- How to test for shoulder mobility, as well as balance and core function

Reading Assignment

Read Chapter 7 of the *ACE Personal Trainer Manual,* 4th edition, paying special attention to the boldface terms in the chapter. After you have read the chapter, define those terms on a separate piece of paper.

Expand Your Knowledge

I.   Why should postural assessments be conducted in addition to movement screens?

_____

_____

_____

_____

_____

II. Define "good posture." _____

_____

_____

III. List the correctible and non-correctible factors that may contribute to muscle imbalances and postural deviations.
   a. Correctible _____

_____

_____

   b. Non-correctible _____

_____

_____

IV. How might a casual conversation with a client help a personal trainer more effectively identify postural deviations during a static postural assessment? _____

_____

_____

V.   You are conducting a screen to identify ankle pronation/supination. Explain what each of the following results would indicate.
   a. The foot collapses inward _____

_____

   b. The foot rolls outward _____

_____

_____

VI. Explain the effects of pronated ankles on the body's kinetic chain. _____

_____

_____

_____

_____

VII. A sedentary lifestyle where the individual spends long hours in a seated position may lead to which of the five common postural deviations covered in this chapter? _____

_____

VIII. What muscles should be suspected to be tight in each of the following scenarios?

a. Anterior tilt of the pelvis _____

b. Posterior tilt of the pelvis _____

c. Forward-head position _____

IX. List the five primary movements that people perform during many daily activities.

a. _____

b. _____

c. _____

d. _____

e. _____

X. What should a personal trainer do if a client experiences pain during a clearing test?

_____

_____

XI. A client is performing the bend and lift screen. Which muscles should be strengthened during the exercise program in response to each of the following observed compensations?

a. The knees move inward _____

b. The back excessively arches _____

c. The ankles collapse inward _____

XII. What is the objective of the hurdle step screen? _____

_____

_____

_____

_____

XIII. Which of the following is **NOT** accurate regarding the shoulder push stabilization screen? Explain your reasoning.

a. _____ Subjects should perform full push-ups, only using modified push-ups if necessary.

b. _____ Clients should be cued to use good technique throughout the screen.

c. _____ Repetitions should be performed slowly.

Explanation: _____

_____

_____

XIV. During the shoulder pull stabilization screen, you note that your client's trunk rotates during the pull. What does this indicate? _____

_____

XV. When performing the Thomas test for hip flexion/quadriceps length, a client is able to keep the back and sacrum flat, but the back of the lowered thigh does touch the table and the knee does not flex to 80 degrees. What muscle should the trainer suspect is tight? _____

XVI. What movements are performed as part of Apley's scratch test for shoulder mobility?

a. _____

b. _____

c. _____

XVII. List the five observations that would mark the termination of the Sharpened Romberg Test.

a. _____

b. _____

c. _____

d. _____

e. _____

XVIII. What aspect of core function is assessed by the blood pressure cuff test? _____

_____

_____

_____

Functional Assessments: Posture, Movement, Core, Balance, and Flexibility

Multiple-choice Questions

1. Which of the following observations would be noted as a postural deviation?
   A. Left and right iliac crests are at same height
   B. The ASIS and pubic bone are in line vertically
   C. The cheek bone is forward of the collar bone
   D. Plumb line passes just anterior to the mastoid process

2. Which of the following postural deviations indicates that a client has medially (internally) rotated shoulders?
   A. Front view: backs of hands are visible
   B. Posterior view: scapular winging visible
   C. Side view: upper back has an exaggerated curve
   D. Front view: sternum not in line with plumb line

3. A client should be referred to his or her physician if which of the following is found during assessments?
   A. Lordosis and kyphosis during postural screening
   B. Limited range of motion during "cobra pose" clearing test
   C. Pain during the shoulder impingement clearing test
   D. Forward-head position during postural screening

4. During the bend and lift screen, which observation would indicate that the client has tight plantarflexors?
   A. Hamstrings touch the calves
   B. Squat initiated at knees
   C. Knees fall inward
   D. Heels raise off the floor

5. During the hurdle step screen, you observe a client exhibiting an anterior pelvic tilt and a forward torso lean as he steps forward. What is this compensation **MOST** indicative of?
   A. Weak gluteus medius and maximus
   B. Tight stance-leg hip flexors
   C. Weak stance-leg hip adductors
   D. Tight ankle plantarflexors

6. During the Thomas test, you observe that your client can easily lower her right thigh to about 10 degrees above the table with the knee flexed at about 90 degrees. Based on these observations, which of the following notes would you make?
   A. Right leg has normal range of motion
   B. Tightness in the right rectus femoris
   C. Limited range of motion in lumbar spine
   D. Tightness in the right iliopsoas

7. Which of the following observations during the passive straight-leg raise represents normal length of the hamstrings?
   A. Raised leg achieves 70 degrees of movement
   B. Pelvis rotates posteriorly after the raised leg passes 70 degrees of movement
   C. Raised leg stops just short of 90 degrees of movement
   D. Opposite leg lifts off the mat as the raised leg approaches 80 degrees of movement

8. While having a client perform the external and internal rotation test, you observe that he can rotate the forearms internally and externally to about 70 degrees, or about 20 degrees off the mat. Based on these observations, which of the following notes would you make?
   A. Good mobility for both internal and external rotators
   B. Tight internal rotators; good mobility for external rotators
   C. Good mobility for internal rotators; tight external rotators
   D. Tightness in both internal and external rotators

9. What is the purpose of stability and mobility training?
   A. Restorative exercise to improve posture and movement compensations
   B. Teaching correct squat, lunge, push, pull, and rotational movement patterns
   C. To prepare the body for sports conditioning and performance training
   D. Rehabilitative exercise to restore function following injury or surgery

10. Scapular winging during the shoulder push stabilization screen would **MOST** likely be due to _____.
    A. Weak core and low back
    B. Scapulothoracic joint instability
    C. Curved thoracic spine
    D. Strong serratus anterior

Show What You Know

I. One of your clients, Eileen, complains of muscle tightness along the left side of her torso. Which common postural deviation might you screen for in an attempt to identify the cause of her discomfort? _____

_____

_____

_____

_____

_____

_____

_____

_____

_____

Practice What You Know

I. Set up a plumb line according the instructions on page 138 and ask a friend or family member to let you observe him or her from the anterior, posterior, sagittal, and transverse views. After noting any postural deviations, think about how you would address those issues in an exercise program.

II. Ask a friend or family member to serve as a subject as you practice the various assessments presented in this chapter. You can even offer this as a free session for an existing client.

CHAPTER 8
Physiological Assessments

Summary Review

A personal trainer should have knowledge and practical skills in both health-related assessments and sports- or skill-related assessments that are relevant to a client's program development and ongoing evaluation.

Testing and Measurement

A personal trainer should have knowledge of the potential resources for gaining hands-on training in fitness assessments.

Personal trainers must be aware of identifiable signs or symptoms that merit immediate exercise-test termination and referral to a qualified healthcare professional.

Anthropometric Measurements and Body Composition

A general understanding of following anthropometric measurements is important for all personal trainers:
- Bioelectrical impedance analysis (BIA)
- Air displacement plethysmography (ADP)
- Dual energy x-ray absorptiometry (DEXA)
- Hydrostatic weighing
- Near-infrared interactance (NIR)
- Total body electrical conductivity (TOBEC)

A personal trainer should have a general understanding of the appropriate use of, protocol for, and programming considerations related to the following anthropometric measurements:
- Skinfold measurement
- Body mass index (BMI)
- Girth measurements
- Waist-to-hip ratio
- Waist circumference

Cardiorespiratory Fitness Testing

For the safe and effective administration of physical-fitness tests, a personal trainer should have knowledge of the following concepts related to cardiorespiratory fitness (CRF) testing:
- Appropriate use of, and reasons for, administering CRF tests
- $\dot{V}O_2$max assessments versus submaximal CRF tests
- Variables related to the lack of accuracy in estimated maximum oxygen uptake assessments
- Methods available for determining maximum heart rate (MHR)
- Cardiorespiratory assessments for the lab or fitness center

A personal trainer should have a general understanding of the appropriate use of, protocol for, and programming considerations related to the following tests:

- Treadmill tests
  - ✓ Bruce submaximal treadmill exercise test
  - ✓ Balke & Ware treadmill exercise test
  - ✓ Ebbeling single-stage treadmill test
- Cycle ergometer tests
  - ✓ YMCA bike test
  - ✓ Astrand-Ryhming (A-R) cycle ergometer test
- Ventilatory threshold tests
  - ✓ Submaximal talk test for VT1
  - ✓ Lactate threshold testing (VT2)
- Field tests
  - ✓ Rockport fitness walking test (1 mile)
  - ✓ 1.5-mile run test
- Step tests
  - ✓ YMCA submaximal step test
  - ✓ McArdle step test

Muscular Fitness Testing

For the safe and effective administration of physical fitness tests, a personal trainer should have knowledge of the following concepts related to muscular fitness testing:

- Appropriate use of, and reasons for, administering muscular fitness tests
- Muscular strength versus muscular endurance
- Health-related benefits of muscular fitness

Muscular Endurance Testing

A personal trainer should have a general understanding of the appropriate use of, protocol for, and programming considerations related to the following muscular endurance tests:

- Push-up test
- Curl-up test
- McGill's torso muscular endurance test battery
  - ✓ Trunk flexor endurance
  - ✓ Trunk lateral endurance
  - ✓ Trunk extensor endurance
- Bodyweight squat test

Muscular Strength Testing

A personal trainer should have a general understanding of the appropriate use of, protocol for, and programming considerations related to the following muscular strength tests:

- 1-RM bench-press test
- 1-RM leg-press test
- 1-RM squat test
- Submaximal strength tests

Sport-skill Assessments

For the safe and effective administration of physical fitness tests, a personal trainer should have knowledge of the appropriate use of, and reasons for administering, sports-skill tests.

Power Testing: Field Tests

A personal trainer should have a general understanding of the appropriate use of, protocol for, and programming considerations related to the following field power tests:

- Anaerobic power
  - ✓ Standing long jump test
  - ✓ Vertical jump test
  - ✓ Kneeling power ball chest launch
- Anaerobic capacity
  - ✓ Margaria-Kalamen stair climb test
  - ✓ 300-yard shuttle run

Speed, Agility, and Quickness Testing

A personal trainer should have a general understanding of the appropriate use of, protocol for, and programming considerations related to the following field speed, agility, and quickness tests:

- Pro agility test
- T-test
- 40-yard dash

Fitness Testing Accuracy

Personal trainers should be familiar with the various causes of fitness test inaccuracy, including:

- Client (test subject)
- Trainer or test technician
- Equipment
- Environment

Getting Started

This chapter covers the various physiological assessments that a personal trainer must be able to perform and interpret in order to create safe and effective exercise programs for clients. After completing this chapter, you will have a better understanding of:

- Body-composition assessments and anthropometric measurements
- Cardiorespiratory fitness assessments, including ventilatory threshold testing and field testing
- Muscular-strength and muscular-endurance testing
- Sports-skill assessments, including tests of power, speed, agility, and quickness

Reading Assignment

Read Chapter 8 of the *ACE Personal Trainer Manual,* 4th edition, paying special attention to the boldface terms in the chapter. After you have read the chapter, define those terms on a separate piece of paper.

Expand Your Knowledge

I. The health-related assessments presented in this chapter focus on what five components?

a. _____

b. _____

c. _____

d. _____

e. _____

II. The skill-related assessments presented in this chapter focus on what six components?

a. _____

b. _____

c. _____

d. _____

e. _____

f. _____

III. List the 10 identifiable signs or symptoms that personal trainers must be aware of during all assessments, as they merit immediate test termination and possible referral to a healthcare professional

a. _____

b. _____

c. _____

d. _____

e. _____

f. _____

g. _____

h. _____

i. _____

j. _____

IV. Explain the difference between the following pairs of words of phrases.

a. Body composition and body mass index _____

_____

b. Overweight and overfat _____

_____

c. Magnetic resonance imaging (MRI) and near-infrared interactance (NIR) _____

_____

d. Android and gynoid _____

_____

V.   About how often should body-composition analysis be performed with a client? _____

_____

_____

VI. At what waist-to-hip ratio is an individual considered to be at risk?

   a. Males _____

   b. Females _____

VII. Define cardiorespiratory fitness. _____

_____

VIII. List four variables that should be constantly assessed and recorded during an exercise test.

   a. _____

   b. _____

   c. _____

   d. _____

IX. Answer the following questions regarding information gathered while interviewing an older-adult client prior to a submaximal treadmill test. *Note:* Each of these scenarios should be considered individually, as they are not meant to collectively describe a single client.

   a. The interview raises no red flags. Which treadmill testing protocol would you choose for this client? _____

   b. The client reveals that he is taking beta blockers. How might this affect the results of the treadmill test? _____

   c. The client mentions that he skipped lunch because he is using his lunch hour as his personal-training session. He has not eaten since before work, several hours earlier. How might this affect the test? _____

_____

X.   List three populations for which cycle ergometer testing is contraindicated.

   a. _____

   _____

   b. _____

   _____

   c. _____

   _____

XI. List two advantages that cycle ergometer testing has over treadmill testing.

   a. _____

   _____

   b. _____

   _____

XII. Mark each of the following descriptions with "VT1" if it corresponds with the first ventilatory threshold or "VT2" if it corresponds with the second ventilatory threshold.

    a. _____ A level of intensity where lactic acid begins to accumulate in the blood

    b. _____ Represents the highest sustainable level of exercise intensity, a strong marker of exercise performance

    c. _____ Below this level of intensity, the cardiorespiratory challenge lies with inspiration and not with expiration

    d. _____ After moving beyond this intensity, ventilation rates begin to increase exponentially as oxygen demands outpace the oxygen-delivery system

    e. _____ A level of intensity at which lactic acid accumulates in the blood at rates faster than the body can buffer and remove it

    f. _____ Testing to determine this metabolic marker is only recommended for well-conditioned individuals with performance goals

XIII. Explain how the results of VT1 testing can be applied to exercise programming. _____

_____

_____

_____

_____

_____

_____

XIV. Explain how the results of VT2 testing can be applied to exercise programming. _____

_____

_____

_____

_____

_____

_____

XV. List five groups of individuals for whom step testing might not be appropriate.

    a. _____

    b. _____

    c. _____

    d. _____

    e. _____

XVI. What does muscular-endurance testing assess? _____

_____

_____

XVII.   A young, athletic client experiences low-back pain during the curl-up assessment, but is able to perform additional repetitions with good form. What is the trainer's appropriate response? _____

_____

_____

XVIII. Why is it important to consider the results of the three components of McGill's battery of torso muscular endurance tests collectively? _____

_____

_____

_____

_____

XIX.   Your client just completed McGill's battery of tests, yielding the following results. Use these results to calculate the ratios below and explain how you would interpret these results.
Flexion: 140 seconds
Extension: 130 seconds
Right-side bridge (RSB): 93 seconds
Left-side bridge (LSB): 95 seconds

a. Flexion:extension ratio _____

b. RSB:LSB ratio _____

c. LSB:extension ratio _____

d. Interpretation _____

_____

_____

XX.   Explain the difference between 1-RM strength testing and submaximal strength testing. ___

_____

_____

_____

XXI.   Define power and explain with what energy system it correlates. _____

_____

_____

XXII.   Power, speed, agility, and quickness assessments should be reserved for what phase of the ACE IFT Model and what type of clients? _____

_____

_____

_____

Multiple-choice Questions

1. Which response would warrant immediate termination of exercise testing?
    A. Ratings of perceived exertion (RPE) >14 (6 to 20 scale)
    B. Heart rate (HR) >age-predicted maximum
    C. Systolic blood pressure (SBP) >220 mmHg
    D. Diastolic blood pressure (DBP) >115 mmHg

2. Which body-composition assessment method produces percent fat estimates that can vary greatly from day to day based on the hydration status of the client being tested?
    A. Skinfolds
    B. Bioelectrical impedance analysis (BIA)
    C. Hydrostatic weighing
    D. Dual energy x-ray absorptiometry (DEXA)

3. You are working with a client who weighs 180 lb (82 kg) with a body-fat percentage of 20%. What will his approximate weight be when he reaches his goal of 15% body fat, assuming that his lean body mass remains constant?
    A. 144 lb (65 kg)
    B. 149 lb (68 kg)
    C. 169 lb (77 kg)
    D. 175 lb (80 kg)

4. Which assessment does not use predicted maximum HR or predicted $\dot{V}O_2$max, but instead provides an actual measured heart rate that corresponds to the client's unique metabolic response to exercise?
    A. YMCA bike test
    B. Bruce submaximal treadmill test
    C. Submaximal talk test for VT1
    D. Rockport fitness walking test

5. Which assessment would be **MOST** appropriate for a 54-year-old male client who has no contraindications for exercise but has not been regularly active in more than 10 years?
    A. McArdle step test
    B. Rockport fitness walking test
    C. VT2 threshold test
    D. Astrand-Ryhming cycler ergometer test

6. What has been shown to be the **BEST** predictor of back health?
    A. Endurance of the core and postural muscles acting on the low back
    B. Range of motion of spinal flexion and extension
    C. Strength of the core and postural muscles acting on the low back
    D. Range of motion of the spinal rotators

7. Which ratio from McGill's torso muscular endurance test battery would be indicative of a muscle imbalance that can lead to back pain?
   A. Flexion:extension ratio of 1.05
   B. Right-side bridge:extension ratio of 0.68
   C. Left-side bridge:flexion ratio of 0.74
   D. Right-side bridge:left-side bridge ratio of 0.97

8. Which of the responses represents the predicted 1-RM bench press for a client who can perform 10 repetitions of the exercise with 150 lb (68 kg) with good form?
   A. 188 lb (85 kg)
   B. 200 lb (91 kg)
   C. 214 lb (97 kg)
   D. 224 lb (102 kg)

9. Which of the following is the **BEST** tool for assessing lower-body muscular strength?
   A. Bodyweight squat test
   B. 10-RM leg press test
   C. Standing long jump test
   D. 1-RM squat test

10. Which of the following assesses anaerobic capacity?
    A. 300-yard shuttle run
    B. Vertical jump test
    C. Pro agility test
    D. 40-yard dash

Show What You Know

I.   A new client would like to establish a realistic weight as his long-term goal. After some discussion, he agrees to think about his weight loss in terms of "fat loss," but still wants to have a goal weight in mind. He currently weighs 230 pounds (104 kg) and has 33% body fat. He would like to get to 29% body fat. What would be this person's goal weight if he is able to maintain his current amount of lean body mass?

    a.   Determine fat weight in pounds _____

    _____

    _____

    b.   Determine lean body weight _____

    _____

    _____

    c.   Calculate goal weight _____

    _____

    _____

Practice What You Know

I.   Ask friends or family members to act as subjects for skinfold measurements and girth measurements. Practice using the skinfold calipers until you are able to get consistent results and accurately calculate the individual's body density. When taking girth measurements, be sure to adhere to the guidelines presented in this chapter. Ask an experience personal trainer to mentor you as you learn these important skills.

II.   Calculate your BMI using the formulas presented on page 185 and compare the results to Table 8-7.

CHAPTER 9
Functional Programming for Stability-Mobility and Movement

Summary Review

Movement
Knowledge of the following terms and concepts related to human movement is essential for all personal trainers:
- Joint mobility versus joint stability
- Factors contributing to movement efficiency
- Movement compensations associated with typical mobility problems
- Length-tension relationships
- Force-couple relationships
- Neural control

Phase 1: Stability and Mobility Training
A personal trainer should have knowledge of the following terms and concepts related to the first phase of functional exercise programming:
- Contributions of slow-twitch and fast-twitch muscle fibers to joint stability and mobility
- Stretching techniques during each phase of a workout session
  - ✓ Myofascial release
  - ✓ Static stretches
  - ✓ Proprioceptive neuromuscular facilitation (PNF)
  - ✓ Active isolated stretches (AIS)
  - ✓ Dynamic and ballistic stretches
- Proximal stability: activating the core
  - ✓ Contribution of each layer of core musculature to spinal stability and mobility
  - ✓ Three-stage model for core and balance training
- Proximal stability: core function
  - ✓ Exercise progression for core activation
  - ✓ Supine drawing-in (centering) exercise
  - ✓ Quadruped drawing-in (centering) with extremity movement exercise
- Proximal mobility: hips and thoracic spine
  - ✓ Fundamental programming principles to improve mobility in the hips and thoracic spine
  - ✓ Exercise progression for core stabilization
  - ✓ Exercises and stretches (and their progressions) to promote mobility in the hips and thoracic spine
- Proximal stability of the scapulothoracic region and distal mobility of the glenohumeral joint
  - ✓ Exercises and stretches (and their progressions) to promote function in the scapulothoracic region and the glenohumeral joint

- Distal mobility of the ankle joint
- Static balance: segmental
  - ✓ Training guidelines for static balance
  - ✓ Specific static-balance exercises and their progressions
- Static balance: integrated (standing)
  - ✓ Stance-position progressions for standing balance exercises

Phase 2: Movement Training

A personal trainer should have knowledge of the following terms and concepts related to the second phase of functional exercise programming:

- The five primary movements that encompass all activities of daily living (ADL)
- The importance of incorporating the five primary movements into a client's exercise programming
- The contribution of the conditions of "glute dominance" and "quad dominance" on human movement patterns
- Exercises and stretches (and their progressions) that train the five primary movement patterns
  - ✓ Bend-and-lift patterns
  - ✓ Single-leg stand patterns
  - ✓ Pushing movements
  - ✓ Pulling movements
  - ✓ Rotational movements
- Dynamic movement patterns over a static base of support

Getting Started

This chapter covers phases 1 and 2 of the functional movement and resistance training component of the ACE Integrated Fitness Training™ (ACE IFT™) Model—stability and mobility training and movement training. After completing this chapter, you will have a better understanding of:

- Length-tension and force-couple relationships
- The various components of stability and mobility training, including core function, proximal mobility and stability, distal mobility, and segmental and integrated balance
- The five primary patterns of movement training—bend-and-lift patterns, single-leg stand patterns, pushing movements, pulling movements, and rotational movements—and how they are addressed in the movement-training phase

Reading Assignment

Read Chapter 9 of the *ACE Personal Trainer Manual*, 4th edition, paying special attention to the boldface terms in the chapter. After you have read the chapter, define those terms on a separate piece of paper.

Expand Your Knowledge

I.   Explain the difference between the following pairs of words or phrases.

    a. Joint stability and joint mobility _____

    _____

    _____

    b. Proximal and distal _____

    _____

    _____

    c. Length-tension relationship and force-couple relationship _____

    _____

    _____

    d. Reciprocal inhibition and synergistic dominance _____

    _____

    _____

    e. "Hollowing" and "bracing" _____

    _____

    _____

    f. Static balance and dynamic balance _____

    _____

    _____

II. Complete the following model of the kinetic chain by marking whether each joint or region primarily demonstrates "mobility" or "stability."

Glenohumeral = _____

Scapulothoracic = _____

Thoracic spine = _____

Lumbar spine = _____

Hip = _____

Knee = _____

Ankle = _____

Foot = _____

III. List four possible causes of muscle shortening, which can contribute to a reduction in a muscle's force-generating capacity.

    a. _____

    b. _____

    c. _____

    d. _____

IV. Describe the potential long-term effect of the following example of synergistic dominance: Tight hip flexors inhibit and weaken the gluteus maximus, forcing the hamstrings to assume a greater role in hip extension. _____

_____

_____

_____

_____

_____

_____

V.   What is the objective of phase 1: stability and mobility training? What is the first step in the process of achieving this objective? _____

_____

_____

VI. List the type of muscle fiber found most in muscles performing each of the following functions and explain why each type is best suited for that function.

a. Muscles responsible for stabilization _____

_____

_____

b. Muscles responsible for joint movement _____

_____

_____

VII. The five programming components of the stability and mobility training phase must be performed in the correct order. Fill in the blanks in the following programming sequence.

a. Proximal stability: _____

b. _____: Pelvis and thoracic spine

c. Proximal stability: _____

Proximal mobility: _____

d. Distal mobility and stability: _____

e. _____

VIII. The term "core" generally refers to muscles in what regions of the body? _____

_____

IX. Describe the function of the muscles that are located in each of the following regions of the core.

a. Deep layer _____

_____

_____

b. Middle layer _____

_____

_____

c. Outer layer _____

_____

_____

X. Describe the emphasis of each portion of the three-stage model for core and balance training.

a. Stage 1: Core function _____

_____

b. Stage 2: Static balance _____

_____

c. Stage 3: Dynamic balance _____

_____

XI. When training for proximal mobility in the hips and thoracic spine, at what point can a client progress from exercises featuring supportive surfaces to ones that are more unsupported in nature? _____

_____

XII. List seven training conditions that can be manipulated by a personal trainer to improve a client's static balance.

a. _____

b. _____

c. _____

d. _____

e. _____

f. _____

g. _____

Multiple-choice Questions

1. Which of the following joints is classified as favoring stability vs. mobility?
    A. Scapulothoracic
    B. Ankle
    C. Thoracic spine
    D. Glenohumeral

2. A lack of hip-joint mobility is **MOST** likely to lead to which of the following?
    A. Hypermobility in the scapulothoracic joints and thoracic spine
    B. Compromised stability in the knees and lumbar spine
    C. Hypermobility in the knee, ankle, and foot joints
    D. Compromised mobility in the knees and lumbar spine

3. Limited movement over an extended period of time, such as is seen with injury and postural deviations, can result in muscle shortening on one side of a joint and muscle lengthening on the other side of the joint. How do these length changes affect the force-generating capacity of these muscles?
    A. The lengthened muscles generally have a higher force production throughout the full range of motion, as muscles are strongest when they are longest
    B. The shortened muscles will produce the same amount of force as they did at normal length, only at a faster rate of movement
    C. They will have greater force-generating capacity at their new lengths, but diminished force-generating capacity at normal resting lengths
    D. They will have diminished force-generating capacity at their new lengths, but greater force-generating capacity at normal resting lengths

4. Which force couple creates posterior pelvic rotation to pull the pelvis out of anterior pelvic tilt?
    A. Hip flexors and erector spinae
    B. Hamstrings and erector spinae
    C. Hip flexors and rectus abdominis
    D. Hamstrings and rectus abdominis

5. The middle layer of torso muscles that are commonly referred to as "the core" consists of the _____.
    A. Multifidi, quadratus lumborum, transverse abdominis, deep fibers of the internal oblique, diaphragm, and pelvic floor musculature
    B. Erector spinae, external oblique, deep fibers of the internal oblique, iliopsoas, rectus abdominis, and latissimus dorsi
    C. Transverse abdominis, diaphragm, interspinali, intertransversarii, and rotatores
    D. Quadratus lumborum, multifidi, external oblique, erector spinae, and pelvic floor musculature

6. Once a client can perform two sets of 10 repetitions of glute bridges, which exercise would provide the **MOST** appropriate progression?
   A. Single-leg glute bridge with a riser under the thoracic spine
   B. Stability ball single-leg glute bridge with opposite knee to chest
   C. Single-leg glute bridge with opposite knee to chest
   D. Stability ball single-leg glute bridge with opposite leg straight

7. When helping a client build scapulothoracic stability, which exercise should a trainer have him or her perform **FIRST** to teach the client how to "pack" the scapula?
   A. Shoulder diagonals without resistance
   B. Supine-lying shoulder depression and shoulder retraction
   C. Prone arm lifts in "I", "Y", "W", and "O" formations
   D. Supine shoulder internal and external rotation with tubing

8. Once a client can demonstrate good static balance while standing on two feet, what exercise could the trainer introduce that would provide the **MOST** appropriate progression?
   A. Reducing points of contact (two feet to one foot)
   B. Balancing on an unstable surface
   C. Raising arms overhead with eyes closed
   D. Narrowing the base of support

9. Which progression follows the part-to-whole teaching strategy in helping a client learn proper technique for the bend-and-lift squatting movement?
   A. Hip hinge → pelvic tilts and back alignment → lower-extremity alignment → figure-4 position
   B. Pelvic tilts and back alignment → figure-4 position → squats with varied foot positions → lunges
   C. Hip hinge → figure-4 position → squats with varied foot positions → squats with arm drivers
   D. Lower-extremity alignment → figure-4 position → squats with arm drivers → lunge matrix

10. Once a client demonstrates good form while performing kneeling wood-chop spiral patterns with short and long moment arms, what exercise would provide the **MOST** appropriate progression?
    A. Standing wood-chops and hay bailers with full rotation
    B. Standing wood-chops and hay bailers with long moment arms
    C. Standing wood-chops and hay bailers with 2-kg medicine ball
    D. Standing wood-chop spiral patterns with short moment arms

Show What You Know

I. Joe is a 42-year-old business executive who hires you after he decides that he would like to start participating in a recreational basketball league with some of his coworkers. He was physically active throughout college and has maintained sporadic bouts of activity since he turned 35. He appears to be 20 pounds (9 kg) overweight. His current activity involves infrequent walks with his wife and golfing two or three times a month with clients. His health history reveals no significant risk factors and he has obtained clearance from his physician to exercise. His current complaints include some mild low-back discomfort, a general lack of conditioning, and a lack of power with his golf drives, which he would like to improve. Initial assessments reveal a need to improve Joe's core conditioning, balance, and posture as foundational components. Joe agrees to train three times each week with these goals in mind. Outline the first three weeks of the core-conditioning portion of Joe's program.

a. Weeks 1–2: Muscle isolation and activation exercises _____

_____

_____

_____

_____

_____

b. Weeks 3–4: Muscle isolation and activation exercises _____

_____

_____

_____

_____

_____

c. Weeks 5–6: Spinal stabilization _____

_____

_____

_____

_____

_____

ACE Personal Trainer Master the Manual

Practice What You Know

I. Practice performing the exercises and stretches illustrated throughout this chapter. Enlist the help of a friend, family member, or client and practice cueing him or her through the various movements. As you study and practice these exercises, focus on the objective listed for each, as this will help you effectively incorporate them into clients' programs. *Note:* Be sure that the individual performing each exercise has the appropriate fitness and skill levels to do so safely and with proper form.

II. Review the five movement patterns addressed in the movement-training phase. As you perform different tasks throughout your day, try to determine which of the five patterns were used to execute that task. Use these examples to illustrate to clients the importance of mastering these patterns.

CHAPTER 10

Resistance Training: Programming and Progressions

Summary Review

Benefits of Resistance Training

Personal trainers should understand the positive impact of resistance training for clients, including the following benefits:
- Increased physical capacity
- Improved physical appearance and body composition
- Enhanced metabolic function
- Decreased injury risk and enhanced disease prevention

Physiological Adaptations to Resistance Training: Acute and Long-term

It is important that personal trainers are familiar with the terms and concepts related to the following physiological adaptations to resistance training:
- Acute adaptations in the nervous and endocrine systems during a resistance-training workout
- Long-term physiological adaptations to progressive resistance exercise (i.e., increased muscle strength and hypertrophy)
- Factors that influence muscle strength and hypertrophy
  - ✓ Hormone levels
  - ✓ Sex
  - ✓ Age
  - ✓ Muscle fiber type
  - ✓ Muscle length
  - ✓ Limb length
  - ✓ Tendon insertion point

Muscular Strength/Power/Endurance Relationships

A personal trainer should be familiar with the following terms and concepts related to muscular strength, power, and endurance:
- Muscular strength versus muscular endurance
- One-repetition maximum (1 RM)
- Muscular power
- Relationship between exercise weightload and muscular power

Training Variables: Factors Affecting Strength Development and Program Design

A personal trainer should be familiar with the following terms and concepts related to the development of a strength-training program:
- Client needs assessment
  - ✓ Health- and skill-related parameters
- Training frequency
- Exercise selection and order
- Training volume

- Appropriate program progressions
- Training intensity
- Training tempo
- Rest intervals

Training Principles
A personal trainer should be familiar with the following resistance-training principles:
- Progression
- Specificity
- Overload
- Reversibility
- Diminishing returns

Resistance-training Periodization Models
A personal trainer should be familiar with the following terms and concepts related to resistance-training periodization models:
- Macrocycles
- Mesocycles
- Microcycles
- Linear versus undulating periodization

Program Design Using the ACE Integrated Fitness Training Model
For safe and effective resistance-training program design, a personal trainer should be familiar with the following terms, concepts, and appropriate rates of progression related to the ACE Integrated Fitness Training™ (ACE IFT™) Model:
- Phase 1: Stability and mobility training
- Phase 2: Movement training
- Phase 3: Load training
- Phase 4: Performance training
  ✓ Client prerequisites for performance training
  ✓ Power lifting versus Olympic lifting
  ✓ Plyometrics for the lower and upper body
  ✓ Movement-pattern progressions for velocity training
  ✓ Speed, power, and agility drills

Special Considerations for Youth and Older Adults
Personal trainers should understand the following factors as they relate to resistance training for youth and older adults:
- Youth strength training
  ✓ Benefits of strength training in youth
  ✓ NSCA guidelines for youth resistance training
- Older adult strength training
  ✓ Benefits of strength training in older adults
  ✓ Exercise precautions and guidelines for older adults

Strength Training Equipment Options
The types of, and appropriate uses for, the following categories of exercise equipment should be understood by all personal trainers:
- Selectorized equipment
- Cables
- Free weights

- Tubing
- Medicine balls
- Bodyweight training

Ergogenic Aids and Supplements

A personal trainer should have basic knowledge of the impact on performance and health-related consequences of consuming the following ergogenic aids and supplements:
- Protein and amino-acid supplements
- β-Alanine (carnosine) and sodium bicarbonate
- Caffeine
- Creatine
- Performance-optimizing vitamins and minerals
- Anabolic-androgenic steroids and related compounds

Common Resistance-training Myths and Mistakes

Personal trainers should have a good understanding of the following common resistance-training myths and mistakes in order to educate their clients about the proper applications and outcomes of regular resistance training:
- "Fat deposits in certain areas can be targeted with strength training via spot reduction."
- "Women will build bulky muscles through weight training."
- "Individuals should use light weights and high repetitions to improve muscle tone, and heavy weights and low repetitions to increase muscle mass."
- "At some point, people get too old to lift weights."
- "Children are too young to lift weights."
- "Free weights are always better than machines."
- "After a person stops resistance training, the muscle turns to fat."
- "Strength training is bad for the exerciser's blood pressure."

Getting Started

This chapter begins by discussing the benefits and acute and long-term physiological adaptations to resistance training. It also covers the resistance-training component of the ACE IFT™ Model, specifically focusing on phases 3 and 4—load training and performance training. After completing this chapter, you will have a better understanding of:
- The various training variables, including frequency, intensity, and rest intervals
- Training principles, including overload, progression, and specificity
- Both linear and undulating periodization programs
- Strength-training equipment options
- Ergogenic aids and supplements

Reading Assignment

Read Chapter 10 of the *ACE Personal Trainer Manual,* 4th edition, paying special attention to the boldface terms in the chapter. After you have read the chapter, define those terms on a separate piece of paper.

Expand Your Knowledge

I. Answer the following questions regarding the benefits of resistance training.
    a. Approximately how much muscle tissue will the average non–strength training adult lose each decade due to disuse atrophy? _____

    _____

    b. How does an inactivity-related decrease in resting metabolic rate (RMR) lead to an increase in body fat? _____

    _____

    c. How might resistance training reduce the risk of colon cancer? _____

    _____

    _____

II. What are the two primary long-term physiological adaptations to progressive resistance exercise? _____

III. Define each of the following terms and explain its effect on muscle contraction force.
    a. Myofibrillar hypertrophy _____

    _____

    b. Sarcoplasmic hypertrophy _____

    _____

    c. Transient hypertrophy _____

    _____

IV. Explain how each of the following factors influences muscular strength and hypertrophy.
    a. Testosterone levels _____

    _____

    b. Sex _____

    _____

    c. Age _____

    _____

    d. Limb length _____

    _____

V. Complete the following equation:
    Muscular strength x Movement speed = _____

VI. List the health- and skill-related parameters that must be considered when developing a client's resistance-training program.

Health-related Parameters   **Skill-related Parameters**

_____   _____

_____   _____

_____   _____

_____   _____

_____   _____

_____

VII. Which of the following weekly strength-training routines would be appropriate for an advanced exerciser performing high-volume/high-intensity workouts?

a. _____ Upper-body exercises on Monday, Wednesday, and Friday, and lower-body and core exercises on Tuesday, Thursday, and Saturday

b. _____ Pushing movements with the chest, shoulders, and triceps on Monday and Thursday, pulling movements with the back, biceps, and trunk on Tuesday and Friday, and squatting and lunging movements with the legs on Wednesday and Saturday

c. _____ Total-body workouts five days a week, with no more than three consecutive days of training

VIII. Give two reasons why training volume should be kept low during the initial stages of a resistance-training program.

a. _____

b. _____

IX. Fill in the blanks.

a. While both volume and intensity are key components of progressive resistance exercise, the most important factor for strength development appears to be _____.

b. It is recommended that the concentric portion of a resistance-training exercise should be performed in _____ seconds and the eccentric muscle action should be performed in _____ seconds.

c. A high-effort set of resistance exercise reduces the muscle's internal energy stores of _____.

d. An individual training with a goal of muscle hypertrophy should incorporate rest intervals of _____, while someone training with a goal of increasing muscular strength should incorporate rest intervals of _____.

X. What are the dangers associated with progressing intensity too quickly? _____

_____

_____

Resistance Training: Programming and Progressions

XI.   Explain the double-progressive strength-training protocol. Give a brief example.

_____

_____

_____

_____

XII.   Define the following training principles.

    a. Specificity _____

    _____

    b. Overload _____

    _____

    c. Reversibility _____

    _____

    d. Diminishing returns _____

    _____

XIII. Briefly explain the difference between linear periodization and undulating periodization.

_____

_____

_____

_____

XIV. What is the primary disadvantage of circuit strength training? What are the advantages?

_____

_____

_____

_____

XV.   Mark each of the following with an "E" if it describes load training for muscular endurance, fitness, and health, an "S" if it describes load training for muscular strength, or an "H" if it describes load training for muscular hypertrophy.

    a. _____ Supersets are often used to save time during workouts, as typical protocols can be quite time-consuming

    b. _____ The exercise performed utilize more type I muscle fibers, and therefore require less recovery between sessions

    c. _____ Training intensity should be between 60 and 70% of maximum resistance

    d. _____ Sessions feature relatively high training volumes and relatively brief rest periods

    e. _____ Training intensity should progress to between 80 and 90% of maximum resistance

    f. _____ Training intensity should be between 70 and 80% of maximum resistance

XVI. Define each of the following terms.
    a. Supersets _____

    _____

    b. Compound sets _____

    _____

    c. Breakdown training _____

    _____

    d. Assisted training _____

    _____

XVII. List the key prerequisites that a client must meet before progressing to phase 4: performance training.
    a. _____
    b. _____
    c. _____
    d. _____
    e. _____
    f. _____
    g. _____

XVIII. Explain how each of the following variables affects the intensity of lower-body plyometric drills.
    a. Points of contact _____

    _____

    b. Speed _____

    _____

    c. Vertical height _____

    _____

    d. Body weight _____

    _____

    e. Complexity of the exercise _____

    _____

XIX. Place the following plyometric drills in order from lowest to highest intensity.
    a. _____ Multiple linear jumps
    b. _____ Single linear jumps
    c. _____ Depth jumps
    d. _____ Hops and bounds
    e. _____ Jumps in place
    f. _____ Multidirectional jumps

XX.   List four ways to progress the intensity of agility drills.

a. _____

b. _____

c. _____

d. _____

XXI.   Match each of the following supplements to its appropriate description.

1. Is marketed for its potential to increase strength, speed recovery, decrease frequency of respiratory infection, and prevent overtraining; research has failed to find a perfor-mance-enhancing benefit

2. Enhances athletic performance, though the brain adapts to chronic use, thereby lessening the effects

3. The liquid remaining after milk had been curdled and strained; a high-quality protein that contains all of the essential amino acids

a. _____ Whey

b. _____ Casein

c. _____ Glutamine

d. _____ ß-alanine

e. _____ Caffeine

f. _____ Creatine

g. _____ Anabolic-androgenic steroid

4. Improves performance by increasing muscle protein synthesis; has harmful side effects ranging from aggression to increased rates of premature death, mostly from suicide and myocardial infarction

5. Acts as a pH buffer in muscle tissue; may delay fatigue and enhance muscle force and power output

6. The source of the white color of milk; accounts for 70 to 80% of milk protein

7. Naturally stored in muscle tissue in small amounts; supplies a rapid burst of energy for an all-out athletic endeavor lasting about five to 10 seconds

XXII.   Match each of the following vitamins and minerals to its appropriate description.

1. Necessary for the synthesis of hemoglobin and myoglobin

2. An essential nutrient for energy production; used most in times of muscular fatigue

3. Important for immune function, protein synthesis, and blood formation

4. Important for the normal metabolism of nerve tissue, protein, fat, and carbohydrate

a. _____ Iron

b. _____ Zinc

c. _____ Vitamin B12

d. _____ Riboflavin

e. _____ Vitamin D

f. _____ Calcium

5. Important for blood clotting, nerve transmission, and muscle stimulation

6. Necessary for calcium absorption, bone growth, and mineralization

Multiple-choice Questions

1. Your new client is a 47-year-old woman who wants to lose weight, but is a bit apprehensive about resistance training because she does not want to "get big." Based on this information, what response would **BEST** facilitate resistance-training program adherence and motivation?
   A. Design a program based on primarily cardiorespiratory exercise with a light (40% 1 RM) circuit with high-repetition (15–25) sets to help her comfortably meet her goals
   B. Tell her that she has nothing to worry about, as women do not produce enough of the male hormone testosterone to "get big"
   C. Show empathy for her concern about getting big and ensure her that you will design a program that will help her to get toned without getting big
   D. Explain the average adult muscle-tissue loss of 5 lb (2.3 kg) per decade, and how resistance training can help her restore lost muscle and raise resting metabolism

2. Strength gains during the first several weeks of a resistance-training program are primarily due to
   _____.
   A. Muscle hypertrophy
   B. Improved neuromuscular function
   C. Enhanced mitochondrial density
   D. Increased myofibrils

3. Which of the following statements is true about the role of type I muscle fibers during resistance-training exercises?
   A. They are responsible for producing quick, high-force movements
   B. They are primarily active during lower levels of force production
   C. They are oxidative and not active during resistance exercises
   D. They are only active when performing 15 or more repetitions

4. Performing which combination of sets, repetitions, and load would result in the **GREATEST** total training volume?
   A. 2 sets x 8 repetitions with 100 pounds (45.5 kg)
   B. 1 set x 12 repetitions with 150 pounds (68.2 kg)
   C. 3 sets x 4 repetitions with 160 pounds (90.9 kg)
   D. 2 sets x 12 repetitions with 90 pounds (40.9 kg)

5. You are working with a new client who wants to begin resistance training in preparation for a one-month backpacking trip he will be taking through the Rocky Mountains. Which of the following training sets and repetition ranges would be **BEST** for helping him prepare for the rigors of this multi-day trip?
   A. 1–2 sets of 8–10 repetitions
   B. 2–4 sets of 4–6 repetitions
   C. 2–3 sets of 12–16 repetitions
   D. 3–5 sets of 6–12 repetitions

6. What work-to-recovery ratio would be **MOST** appropriate to include in a resistance-training circuit for small-group personal-training sessions with clients who have primary goals that require enhanced muscular endurance?
   A. 75-second work interval:15-second recovery interval
   B. 90-second work interval:2–3 minute recovery interval
   C. 90-second work interval:60-second recovery interval
   D. 75-second work interval:3–5 minute recovery interval

7. The resistance-training program you have designed for a client has her performing 8–12 repetitions during each set, using a double-progressive training protocol for advancing workload. During her most recent personal-training session, she was able to perform two sets of 12 repetitions on the leg press machine with 200 lb (90.9 kg). Based on this information, what would be the **MOST** appropriate progression for her on the leg press exercise?
   A. Increase weight to 220 lb (100 kg) and work toward 12 repetitions at this new weight
   B. Continue with current weight until reaching 15 repetitions per set, then increase weight by 10%
   C. Increase weight to 210 lb (95.5 kg) and work toward 12 repetitions at this new weight
   D. Raise the weight to 240 lb (109.1 kg) and perform eight repetitions

8. Which of the following programs would be **MOST** appropriate for a client who has a primary focus on improving muscular strength?
   A. Two sets of 4–8 repetitions for each major muscle group or movement pattern, utilizing a split routine that allows 72–96 hours of recovery time before working the same muscle group again
   B. Two sets of 8–12 repetitions for each major movement pattern, utilizing a three-day undulating periodization model for full-body training with 48 hours of recovery time between workouts
   C. Three sets of 8–10 repetitions for each major muscle group or movement pattern, utilizing a split routine that allows 48–72 hours of recovery time before working the same muscle group again
   D. Three sets of 3–5 repetitions on explosive, full-body exercises performed 3 days per week with 48–72 hours of recovery time between workouts

9. You are working with a client who wants to train for a specific athletic competition. Before progressing this client to performance training (phase 4), what criteria should he meet to allow for a safe and effective transition to this type of training?
   A. Successful completion of stability and mobility training followed by 12 weeks of load training
   B. Good postural stability, proper movement patterns, and relatively high levels of strength
   C. Successful completion of stability and mobility training and movement training
   D. Regular participation in resistance training for at least three consecutive years

10. What plyometric drill would provide the **MOST** appropriate progression for a client who can successfully perform a predetermined number of vertical jumps and single linear jumps?
    A. Depth jumps
    B. Multidirectional jumps
    C. Hops and bounds
    D. Multiple linear jumps

Show What You Know

I.   You have three clients, Manny, Andre, and Matt, who work out together in a small-group training session. Using the following information regarding their performance of the incline bench press exercise, answer the questions below.

Manny: Three sets of 12 repetitions with 180 pounds

Andre: Four sets of 8 repetitions with 210 pounds

Matt: Three sets of 4 repetitions with 255 pounds

a.   Determine each of their training volumes specific to the incline bench press exercise.

Manny _____

Andre _____

Matt _____

b.   Who is likely to have used the most energy and burned the most calories during the performance of this exercise? Why? _____

_____

Practice What You Know

I.   If you have clients who can appropriately train in the performance-training phase, slowly incorporate the various speed and agility drills presented in this chapter. Not only will this provide a great workout, but it will also give you an opportunity to practice the setup, cueing, and recording of results for each drill. *Note:* Many of these drills are included on the CD-Rom included at the back of the *ACE Personal Trainer Manual,* 4th edition.

II.   Review the strength-training equipment options presented on pages 356–357 and think about how you can use them to add variety to the workouts of your existing clients, being sure to consider each client's level of health and experience, as well as his or her training goals.

III.   Review the resistance-training myths and mistakes presented on pages 358–363. Have you ever heard these myths or encountered these mistakes while working at a fitness facility? Formulate ways in which you can respond if you do.

CHAPTER 11

Cardiorespiratory Training: Programming and Progressions

Summary Review

Physiological Adaptations to Acute and Chronic Cardiorespiratory Exercise

For safe and effective exercise programming, personal trainers must have knowledge of the fundamental physiological adaptations to cardiorespiratory exercise related to the following topic areas:

- Muscular system
- Cardiovascular system
- Respiratory system
- Time required for increases in aerobic capacity
- Physiological adaptations to steady-state and interval-based exercise

Components of a Cardiorespiratory Workout Session

A personal trainer should have knowledge of the concepts related to the following components of a cardiorespiratory workout session:

- Warm-up
- Conditioning phase
  ✓ Cardiovascular drift
- Cool-down

General Guidelines for Cardiorespiratory Exercise for Health, Fitness, and Weight Loss

A personal trainer should be familiar with the following terms and concepts related to cardiorespiratory exercise programming and understand the impact of each on a client's acute and long-term exercise performance:

- *2008 Physical Activity Guidelines for Americans* by the U.S. Department of Health & Human Services
- Physical-activity guidelines from the American College of Sports Medicine (ACSM) and the American Heart Association (AHA)
- F.I.T.T. acronym
- F.I.T.T.E. acronym
- Frequency
- Intensity
  ✓ Cardiovascular recommendations for healthy adults
  ✓ Recommended framework for exercise intensity for apparently healthy adults
- Heart rate
- Karvonen formula
- Ratings of perceived exertion

Cardiorespiratory Training: Programming and Progressions

- $\dot{V}O_2$ or metabolic equivalents
- First ventilatory threshold (VT1)
- Second ventilatory threshold (VT2)
- Caloric expenditure
- Talk test
- Blood lactate and VT2
  - ✓ Training zones (1 through 3)
- Duration
- Exercise progression
  - ✓ Recommendations for exercise duration and quantity
- Fartlek training

Modes or Types of Cardiorespiratory Exercise

A personal trainer should be knowledgeable about the following terms and concepts related to modes of cardiorespiratory exercise and the appropriateness of each for individual clients:
- Physical activities that promote improvement or maintenance of cardiorespiratory fitness
- Equipment-based cardiovascular exercise
- Group exercise
- Circuit training
- Outdoor exercise
- Seasonal exercise
- Water-based exercise
- Mind-body exercise
- Lifestyle exercise

ACE Integrated Fitness Training™ Model—Cardiorespiratory Training Phases

A personal trainer should have an understanding of the training focus and program-design considerations for each phase of the ACE Integrated Fitness Training (ACE IFT™) Model:
- Phase 1: Aerobic-base training
- Phase 2: Aerobic-efficiency training
- Phase 3: Anaerobic-endurance training
- Phase 4: Anaerobic-power training

Recovery and Regeneration

A personal trainer should be familiar with the concepts related to recovery and regeneration and understand the impact of each on a client's acute and long-term exercise performance.

Special Considerations for Youth and Older Adults

A personal trainer should have an understanding of the following terms and concepts related to the unique training considerations for youth and older adults:
- Youth
  - ✓ Overspecialization
  - ✓ Orthopedic trauma
- Older adults
  - ✓ Cardiovascular risk
  - ✓ Orthopedic risk
  - ✓ Preservation of muscle tissue
  - ✓ The rate at which older individuals adapt to training

Getting Started

This chapter features a discussion of the physiological adaptations to acute and chronic cardiorespiratory exercise. It also includes coverage of the cardiorespiratory-training phases of the ACE IFT Model. After completing this chapter, you will have a better understanding of:
- How cardiorespiratory exercise affects the following systems: muscular, cardiovascular, and respiratory
- The components of a well-designed cardiorespiratory-training session
- General guidelines for cardiorespiratory exercise
- Various modes of cardiorespiratory exercise
- Special considerations for youth and older adults

Reading Assignment

Read Chapter 11 of the *ACE Personal Trainer Manual*, 4th edition, paying special attention to the boldface terms in the chapter. After you have read the chapter, define those terms on a separate piece of paper.

Expand Your Knowledge

I.   Fill in the blanks.
   a. During low-intensity endurance exercise, _____ muscle fibers will undergo adaptations, including increases in the size and number of _____ within the cell to augment aerobic adenosine triphosphate (ATP) production.

   b. During high-intensity endurance exercise, _____ muscle fibers may also be recruited, and will adapt primarily by increasing the number of anaerobic _____ so that anaerobic energy production will be enhanced.

   c. Due to the expansion of blood volume that occurs with endurance training, the heart muscle will _____, enlarging its chambers and becoming a bigger and stronger muscle that is able to deliver a higher _____ to the muscles.

   d. Both the _____ and _____ of the respiratory muscles improve with cardiorespiratory training.

   e. _____, the traditional standard marker of the aerobic-training effect, increases with training, but reaches a peak and plateaus within six months. However, increases in _____, a significant marker of metabolism, may continue for years.

II. When do the cardiovascular adaptations to exercise begin? _____
   _____

III. When clients mention "getting a second wind," what physiological marker has been reached? What determines how long it takes a client to reach his or her "second wind"?
   _____
   _____
   _____

IV. Which of the following is the primary reason for including a cool-down period during every workout?
   a. _____ To return the body's core temperature to pre-exercise levels
   b. _____ To improve flexibility and reduce muscle soreness
   c. _____ To prevent blood from pooling in the extremities
   d. _____ To increase the "muscle pump" experienced after an intense workout

V. List the four general exercise guidelines for adults 18 to 64 years of age.
   a. _____

   _____

   b. _____

   _____

   c. _____

   _____

   d. _____

   _____

VI. List three specific exercise guidelines for children 6 to 17 years of age.
   a. _____

   _____

   b. _____

   _____

   c. _____

   _____

VII. Which three elements of the F.I.T.T.E. acronym collectively represent the exercise load or volume? _____

VIII. Match each of the following methods that trainers can use to program and monitor exercise intensity with its appropriate descriptions.

1. A subjective method of gauging exercise intensity

2. Separates zone 2 from zone 3 in the three-zone training model

3. Involves using multiples of an assumed average metabolic rate of 3.5 mL/kg/min

4. Discrepancies in individual resting heart rates are taken into account when using this method

5. Probably the most widely used approach for programming and monitoring exercise intensity, though its use is strongly discouraged

6. Calculated by measuring or estimating the total quantity of O_2 consumed per minute and multiplying it by 5 kcal/liter O_2

7. Because of the debate regarding body position when measuring resting heart rate when using this method, two sets of training zones may be necessary, one for seated/recumbent positions and one for standing positions

8. Use of this marker of intensity requires an estimation attained via a mathematical formula that has high degree of inherent error

9. Is associated (in most healthy people) with a flattening of the heart-rate response to increasing intensity

10. Although the evidence base for this method is very deep, the very large range of acceptable percentages makes it difficult to use when recommending exercise intensities

11. Works on the premise that about at the intensity of VT1, the increase in ventilation is accomplished by an increase in breathing frequency

12. Does not correlate strongly with performance and is generally not influenced by training

13. Very sedentary individuals often find this difficult to use, as they find any level of exercise fairly hard

14. Discrepancies in individual resting heart rates are *not* taken into account, which means that this approach often under- or overestimates appropriate exercise intensities

15. Though this is considered the "gold standard," it may be less useful than widely believed

16. Moderate = 70% MHR; Somewhat hard = 80% MHR; Hard = 85% MHR

17. Is based on an individual's unique metabolic or ventilatory responses

a. _____ %MHR

b. _____ %HRR

c. _____ RPE

d. _____ $\dot{V}O_2$

e. _____ METs

f. _____ Caloric expenditure

g. _____ Talk test

h. _____ VT2

IX. List the three exercise duration guidelines for overweight and obese individuals, or those seeking to control their weight, provided by the U.S. Department of Health & Human Services.

   a. _____

   _____ *or*

   b. _____

   _____ *or*

   c. _____

   _____

X.   When working with a beginner client, what is the most appropriate progression variable to manipulate initially? _____

   _____

XI. Why might water-based be contraindicated for a client with circulatory issues?

   _____

   _____

XII. List the four cardiorespiratory-training phases of the ACE IFT Model.

   a. Phase 1 _____

   b. Phase 2 _____

   c. Phase 3 _____

   d. Phase 4 _____

XIII. In what phase of cardiorespiratory training should each of the following assessments be conducted?

   a. Talk test for VT1 _____

   b. VT2 threshold test _____

XIV. Answer the following questions regarding the four phases of the ACE IFT Model.

   a. What is the primary training focus of phase 1: aerobic-base training? _____

   _____

   b. At what point can clients progress to phase 2: aerobic-efficiency training? _____

   _____

   c. What is the primary training focus of phase 2? _____

   _____

   d. At what point can clients progress to phase 3: anaerobic-endurance training? _____

   _____

   e. What is the primary training focus of phase 3? _____

   _____

   f. What type of clients will progress to phase 4: anaerobic-power training? _____

   _____

XV. Trainers working with clients in phase 1 of the ACE IFT Model do not complete any cardiorespiratory fitness assessments before beginning the training program. That being the case, what can trainers use to establish the upper limit for exercise intensity?_____

_____

_____

XVI. What is the primary cardiorespiratory training phase for regular exercisers in a fitness facility who have goals for improving or maintaining fitness and/or weight loss? _____

_____

_____

XVII. Zone 2 intervals performed during phase 2 cardiorespiratory training provide a stimulus that will eventually increase a client's heart rate at VT1. What are the results of this increase? _____

_____

_____

XVIII. Explain why zone 2 (i.e., between VT1 and VT2) is sometimes described as a "black hole" intensity by competitive athletes. _____

_____

_____

_____

XIX. When working with older adults, what are the four overriding concerns that dictate modifications of an exercise program?

a. _____

b. _____

c. _____

d. _____

Cardiorespiratory Training: Programming and Progressions

Multiple-choice Questions

1. When performing steady-state cardiorespiratory exercise, which of the following is **LEAST** likely to limit exercise duration?
   A. Availability of oxygen
   B. Availability of energy from stored fat and/or free fatty acids
   C. The willingness to continue
   D. Availability of energy from stored glycogen and/or blood glucose

2. What causes cardiovascular drift?
   A. Increased heart rate to compensate for reduced blood volume due to sweat production for thermoregulation
   B. Decreased heart rate resulting from an inability to sustain cardiac output due to fatigue
   C. Increased stroke volume to compensate for reduced blood volume due to sweat production for thermoregulation
   D. Decreased stroke volume resulting from an inability to sustain cardiac output due to fatigue

3. What is the **PRIMARY** reason for having all clients perform an adequate cool-down?
   A. To prevent delayed onset muscle soreness (DOMS)
   B. To perform static stretching for enhanced flexibility
   C. To enhance venous return to prevent blood pooling in the extremities
   D. To maintain increased caloric expenditure to enhance weight loss

4. What is the **GREATEST LIMITATION** associated with using heart-rate reserve (HRR) to calculate exercise target heart rate?
   A. Target heart rate must be calculated as a %HRR using the Karvonen formula
   B. Accurate programming using HRR requires actual measured maximum heart rate (MHR) and resting heart rate
   C. New MHR prediction equations are more accurate than MHR = 220 – age
   D. Exercise percentages were established through population-based research

5. Which of the following weekly training plans would have a session RPE of 450 points?
   A. 4 sessions x 25 minutes at an RPE of 5
   B. 2 sessions x 30 minutes at an RPE of 5 and 2 sessions x 20 minutes at an RPE of 3
   C. 3 sessions x 30 minutes at an RPE of 5
   D. 2 sessions x 30 minutes at an RPE of 4 and 3 sessions 20 minutes at an RPE of 4.5

6. During cardiorespiratory exercise with progressively increasing intensity, the need for additional oxygen is met initially through linear increases in minute ventilation ($\dot{V}_E$). The point at which the increased demands for oxygen can no longer be met by this linear increase, causing a nonlinear increase in ventilation is known as the _____ and can be measured via a _____.
   A. Aerobic capacity; $\dot{V}O_2$ max test
   B. Second ventilatory threshold (VT2); VT2 threshold test
   C. Onset of blood lactate accumulation (OBLA); blood lactate analyzer
   D. First ventilatory threshold (VT1); submaximal talk test for VT1

7. Which of the following corresponds with the second ventilatory threshold (VT2)?
    A. Talk test threshold
    B. Onset of blood lactate accumulation (OBLA)
    C. Aerobic capacity
    D. The dividing point between zone 1 and zone 2

8. What is the **PRIMARY** focus of aerobic-base training in the ACE IFT Model?
    A. Creating positive experiences and early success through achievable zone 1 exercise of increasing duration
    B. Progressively increasing zone 2 intervals to intensities just below VT2
    C. Building a strong endurance base as part of a periodization plan for performance in long-distance events
    D. Transitioning from training for improved health to training for improved fitness

9. Most fitness enthusiasts that exercise in a gym or at home on a regular basis on multiple days per week will spend many years reaching their fitness goals through aerobic-efficiency training. Research with these well-trained non-athletes has found that they will spend as much as ___% of their total training time in zone 2.
    A. 10
    B. 25
    C. 35
    D. 50

10. Which of the following training scenarios would **MOST** likely result in overtraining syndrome for an endurance athlete?
    A. Increasing the intensity of zone 3 intervals by 10% from one week to the next
    B. Decreasing the number of recovery days per week to accommodate additional interval work
    C. Increasing the duration of zone 1 training by 20% over the course of three weeks
    D. Decreasing the total time spent doing zone 2 interval work when increasing the intensity

Show What You Know

I. One of your more advanced clients, who performs some very high-intensity intervals during the cardiorespiratory condition phase of her workouts, likes to stretch at the beginning of the warm-up period. Explain how this practice can not only negatively impact her performance, but also potentially be harmful. _____

    _____

    _____

    _____

    _____

    _____

    _____

    _____

II. Respond to the following scenarios involving clients who are not achieving the results they hoped for from their cardiorespiratory-training programs.

a. Dave is an avid runner, but wanted to take a break from his demanding running program. To provide some variety while still maintaining his cardiorespiratory fitness, Dave decided to try biking and swimming as alternate modes of exercise for a few months. After recently returning to his running program, he has noticed a decline in his performance. Why might that be the case? _____

_____

_____

_____

_____

_____

_____

b. Kevin performs resistance training three days per week, but really dislikes cardiorespiratory exercise. He does enjoy playing sports on the weekend, so he decided to increase the number of days he plays basketball from one to three days a week. After adhering to this routine for several months, Kevin decides to start running on the treadmill as the weather starts to turn cold. He realizes that he is tired after only a few minutes of running, just as he was several months earlier when doing the same exercise, and he is very disappointed in the lack of improvement in his performance. Explain the lack of improvement in Kevin's performance. _____

_____

_____

_____

_____

_____

Practice What You Know

Study the sample programs presented in the tables throughout this chapter and think about how you can improve the exercise programs you are using with your current clients. Are your less-fit clients working above VT1, thus increasing their risk for injury? Are your more-fit clients doing too much work in zone 2 (between VT1 and VT2), and therefore wasting energy in the "black hole"?

CHAPTER 12

The ACE Integrated Fitness Training™ Model in Practice

Summary Review

This chapter presents six case studies featuring the types of clients that many personal trainers will work with on a daily basis in most fitness facilities. This content offers practical examples that should help you synthesize the material presented in Chapters 5 through 11. Each case study provides a scenario in which a personal trainer has to determine a client's current stage of behavior change, conduct the most effective assessments for the client, and design an exercise program based on the results of the assessments that will also meet the client's goals.

Case Study 1: Sharon
- 33-year-old woman who works from home, has two children under the age of four, and would like to return to her pre-pregnancy fitness level

Case Study 2: David
- 57-year-old business executive and avid recreational athlete who hires a personal trainer to help improve his golf game

Case Study 3: Jan
- 17-year-old female athlete who wants to improve her chances of attaining a volleyball scholarship

Case Study 4: Stanley
- 28-year-old sedentary male who wants to lose weight and improve his overall health

Case Study 5: Meredith
- 64-year-old woman with arthritis who hires a trainer to help her get back in shape and improve her tennis game

Case Study 6: Kelly
- 30-year-old professional woman who wants to lose weight and improve her appearance for her upcoming wedding

Getting Started

The case studies featured in this chapter are designed to enable trainers to identify, develop, and implement programs at the various physiological stages of the ACE IFT™ Model. After completing this chapter, you will have a better understanding of:

- How to apply the theoretical knowledge presented in Chapters 5 through 11 in a real-world scenario
- How to interpret assessment results and apply what was learned during the exercise programming process
- How to overcome adherence obstacles when working with clients
- How program modifications can help clients achieve their goals

Reading Assignment

Read Chapter 12 of the *ACE Personal Trainer Manual*, 4th edition, paying special attention to the boldface terms in the chapter. After you have read the chapter, define those terms on a separate piece of paper.

Multiple-choice Questions

USE THE FOLLOWING CLIENT INFORMATION TO ANSWER QUESTIONS 1–5:

Client:	Male, age = 38 years
Family history:	Father was diagnosed with hypertension at 53 years of age
Smoking:	Quit smoking 12 years ago
Height:	70 in (1.78 m)
Weight:	195 lb (88.6 kg)
BMI:	28 kg/m²
Blood pressure:	137/86 mmHg
Total serum cholesterol:	221 mg/dL
Fasting plasma glucose:	98 mg/dL
Current exercise:	Resistance training 60 to 90 minutes per day for the past 7 years, following a five day per week split routine consisting of: chest/shoulders/triceps (2 days/week), back/biceps/core (2 days/week), and legs (1 day/week); warm-up consisting of 10 minutes on the elliptical machine (moderate pace), and cool-down consisting of 5 minutes of stretching for hamstrings
Goals:	Recently told by his physician that he is prehypertensive and needs to reduce his total cholesterol. He is worried about having high blood pressure like his father and does not want to go on medication for cholesterol. He would also like to lose about 10 lb (4.5 kg) of body fat while increasing his muscular strength and size. He is planning to train with you two sessions per week for 12 weeks to start.
Initial assessment results:	Postural screen: Revealed internal rotation of the shoulders and lordosis
	Movement and flexibility assessments: Revealed lack of ROM in shoulder external rotation and flexion, a lack of ROM in hip flexion (passive straight-leg raise), and lack of ROM and extension of lumbar spine during the Thomas test
	Trunk endurance tests: Flexion = 80 seconds; extension = 50 seconds; right-side bridge = 50 seconds; left-side bridge = 48 seconds

1. According to the ACSM risk stratification, what is this client's level of risk?
   A. Low risk
   B. Moderate risk
   C. High risk
   D. Very high risk

2. Based on the ACE IFT Model, what cardiorespiratory assessment would be **MOST** appropriate for this client at this time?
   A. Submaximal talk test for VT1
   B. Rockport fitness walking test
   C. No assessment necessary at this time
   D. VT2 threshold test

3. Based on this client's current exercise and fitness, what would be the **MOST** appropriate initial cardiorespiratory program to help him work toward his goals?
   A. Extend warm-up to 15 minutes of steady-state exercise in zone 1, progressively increase duration to 20–30 continuous minutes in zone 1, and then progress to phase 2: aerobic-efficiency training
   B. Begin with cardiorespiratory programming in phase 2: aerobic-efficiency training, with a primary focus on progressing from low-zone 2 intervals to high-zone 2 intervals to boost caloric expenditure
   C. Increase to 20 minutes of continuous zone 1 exercise with brief 1-minute intervals (1:3 work-to-recovery intervals). Progress duration to 30 minutes while increasing interval length, and then progress to phase 2: aerobic-efficiency training
   D. Extend warm-up to 15 minutes, with a 5-minute zone 2 interval in the middle and add a 10-minute cool-down with intensity in zone 1 to increase cardiorespiratory training time to boost caloric expenditure

4. Based on this client's trunk endurance test results, in which of the following ratios did his performance meet the criteria for balanced endurance among the muscle groups tested?
   A. Flexion:extension ratio
   B. Right-side bridge:left-side bridge ratio
   C. Right-side bridge:extension ratio
   D. Left-side bridge:extension ratio

5. Based on the information provided above, what would be the appropriate initial functional movement and resistance training program for this client?
   A. Progress current program using an undulating periodization model, and add a dynamic warm-up to improve core stability
   B. Train proper techniques for squatting, lunging, pushing, pulling, and rotation through movement training (phase 2)
   C. Implement a new load training (phase 3) split routine with an expanded flexibility focus during the cool-down
   D. Work on postural stability, core strength and function, and flexibility through stability and mobility training (phase 1)

ACE Personal Trainer Master the Manual

USE THE FOLLOWING CLIENT INFORMATION TO ANSWER QUESTIONS 6–10:

Client:	Female, age = 27 years
Family history:	Mother has osteoporosis; father had coronary bypass surgery at age 52
Smoking:	Non-smoker
Height:	64 in (1.63 m)
Weight:	122 lb (55.5 kg)
BMI:	21 kg/m²
Blood pressure:	114/68 mmHg
Total serum cholesterol:	168 mg/dL
LDL cholesterol:	95 mg/dL
HDL cholesterol:	64 mg/dL
Fasting plasma glucose:	87 mg/dL
Current exercise:	Runs five days per week, with the following distribution: 30-minute run at lunch on Mondays, Wednesdays, and Fridays; long run of 90 minutes on Saturdays; and 60-minute run with a local running group on Sundays. Warm-up consists of five minutes of yoga sun salutations followed by a five-minute walk. Cool-down consists of five minutes of walking plus 10 minutes of static stretching on weekdays and 20 minutes of static stretching on weekends.
Goals:	Wants to begin resistance training to reduce her risk for developing osteoporosis, look more "toned," and increase strength for running and injury prevention. Also would like to improve posture to address the neck and low-back soreness she feels when working extended hours at the computer. She signs up for two personal-training sessions per week for eight weeks.
Initial assessment results:	Postural screen: Revealed kyphosis with slight anterior pelvic tilt
	Movement and flexibility assessments: Revealed good ROM in all shoulder movements, hip flexion (passive straight-leg raise), Thomas test, but limited thoracic mobility. Movement during the bend and lift test was initiated with forward knee movement and she was unable to reach the figure-4 position, as her heels lifted off the ground. Good movement and balance during the hurdle step screen.
	Trunk endurance tests: Flexion = 40 seconds; extension = 60 seconds; right-side bridge = 46 seconds; left-side bridge = 44 seconds

6. According to the ACSM risk stratification, what is this client's "Total Score" for atherosclerotic cardiovascular disease and associated level of risk?
   A. Total score = 0; low risk
   B. Total score = +1; low risk
   C. Total score = +1; moderate risk
   D. Total score = +2; moderate risk

7. Based on the ACE IFT Model, what cardiorespiratory assessment would be **MOST** appropriate for this client at this time?
   A. Bruce submaximal treadmill exercise test
   B. Submaximal talk test for VT1
   C. VT2 threshold test
   D. No assessment necessary at this time

8. Based on this client's trunk endurance test results, in which of the following ratios did her performance fail to meet the criteria for balanced endurance among the muscle groups tested?
   A. Flexion:extension ratio
   B. Right-side bridge:left-side bridge ratio
   C. Right-side bridge:extension ratio
   D. Left-side bridge:extension ratio

9. Based on the information provided above, what would be the appropriate initial functional movement and resistance training program for this client?
   A. Recommend a group strength class that she can attend for four weeks to help her build initial muscular endurance before beginning her personal-training sessions
   B. Implement a program designed to improve posture and core strength and function through stability and mobility training (phase 1)
   C. Focus initially on developing proper techniques for squatting, lunging, pushing, pulling, and rotation through movement training (phase 2)
   D. Design an initial load training (phase 3) program with 2 sets of 12–16 repetitions on 6–10 machine-based exercises to build initial strength before progressing to more functional exercise

10. Based on this client's performance during the bend and lift screen, what limitations are **MOST** likely preventing her from correctly performing this screen?
    A. Weak core musculature and tight hamstrings
    B. Gluteal group dominance and tight dorsiflexors
    C. Weak quadriceps and plantarflexors
    D. Quadriceps and hip flexor dominance and tight plantarflexors

Practice What You Know

I. Spend some time carefully studying the six case studies presented in this chapter. Use them to fine-tune your understanding of how to apply the ACE IFT Model, and try to draw from your own experience and current clientele as you interpret the choices made by the trainer in each scenario. Mastering the theoretical knowledge presented in the preceding chapters is not enough to make you a successful personal trainer; you must know how to synthesize that information and create fitness programs that take into account all aspects of each client's wants and needs, both physically and psychologically.

II. If applicable, think about each of your current clients. Where do they fall on the health—fitness—performance continuum? How can the principles of the ACE IFT Model help in their current programs? What modifications can you make to better assist them as they work toward their goals? And finally, what can you do to improve the training programs you currently offer?

CHAPTER 13
Mind-body Exercise

Summary Review

Personal trainers should have a basic understanding of the essential tenets of mind-body exercise, including the following terms and concepts:
- Neurobiological foundations of mind-body exercise
- Roots of contemporary mind-body exercise programs
- Differentiating characteristics of mind-body exercise
- Research-supported outcomes and benefits of mind-body exercise
- Common components of mind-body exercise programs
- Mind-body exercise modalities and programs
  - ✓ Yoga
  - ✓ Qigong exercise
  - ✓ Tai chi
- Contemporary mind-body exercise programs
  - ✓ Pilates
  - ✓ Alexander Technique
  - ✓ Feldenkrais Method
  - ✓ Nia
  - ✓ Native American and Alaskan spiritual dancing

Assessing Outcomes

A personal trainer should be aware of various methods used to objectively measure the response to mind-body exercise, including the following:
- Quality of life
- Blood pressure
- Pulmonary function
- Balance control
- Anxiety and tension
- Spirituality

Indications for Mind-body Exercise

Personal trainers can utilize a number of common indications for recommending mind-body exercise for their clients, including the following:
- Mind-body exercise and chronic disease management
- Mind-body modalities and acute coronary syndromes

Getting Started

This chapter reviews many of the popular forms of mind-body exercise, both classical and contemporary, and offers practical suggestions for how trainers can incorporate mind-body techniques into training sessions. It also explains the research-supported outcomes and benefits of mind-body exercise. After completing this chapter, you will have a better understanding of:

- The neurological foundations of mind-body exercise
- The classical forms of mind-body exercise—yoga, tai chi, and qigong
- The roots of contemporary forms of mind-body exercise, including Pilates and Nia
- The role of mind-body exercise in chronic disease management
- The general precautions associated with each of these types of exercise

Reading Assignment

Read Chapter 13 of the *ACE Personal Trainer Manual*, 4th edition, paying special attention to the boldface terms in the chapter. After you have read the chapter, define those terms on a separate piece of paper.

Expand Your Knowledge

I. Fill in the blanks.

    a. Any form or level of physical activity can be "mind-body," but _____ physical activity may provide a preferable platform for _____ benefits.

    b. Mind-body exercise can be described as physical exercise executed with a profound _____.

    c. The Asian _____ and _____ disciplines are at the root of most contemporary mind-body programs.

    d. Because of its slow contemplative nature, _____ can help reduce anxiety, blood pressure, and symptoms of depression.

    e. The _____ is frequently cited as the primary centering activity in mind-body exercise.

    f. Because some yoga programs involve advanced breathing techniques (e.g., breath retentions and breath suspensions), caution must be used with those who have _____ or _____ disease.

II. List six possible benefits of regular participation in mind-body exercise.

    a. _____

    b. _____

    c. _____

    d. _____

    e. _____

    f. _____

III. According to the *Yoga Sutra*, yoga is composed of what eight components, or "limbs"?

    a. _____

    b. _____

    c. _____

    d. _____

    e. _____

    f. _____

    g. _____

    h. _____

IV. Match each of the following terms with the appropriate definition or description.

1. The physical arm of yoga

2. The primary Chinese methodology for activating the "medicine within"

3. Moving meditation

4. Emphasizes precise anatomical alignment and the frequent use of props

5. Easier and more relaxing for those who are relatively weak, fatigued, and experiencing peak stressful periods in life

6. The principal purpose is to awaken the "serpent power" with posture, breath control, chanting, and meditation

7. The practice of voluntary breath control

8. An easier form of tai chi, with smaller steps and movements that involve less twisting and impose less stress on the legs and knees

a. _____ Qigong	
b. _____ Feldenkrais Method	
c. _____ Restorative yoga	
d. _____ Hatha yoga	
e. _____ Tai chi	
f. _____ Sun style	
g. _____ Nia	
h. _____ Kundalini yoga	
i. _____ Pranayama	
j. _____ Iyengar yoga	
k. _____ Alexander Technique	
l. _____ Wu style	
m. _____ Pilates	

9. A form of tai chi featuring a high stance, making it easier for older people to learn

10. Based on the idea that there is a core set of postural muscles that help to keep the body balanced and are essential to providing good support to the spine

11. A method that teaches the transformation of neuromuscular habits by helping an individual focus on sensory experiences

12. Combines "Awareness Through Movement" and "Functional Integration"

13. Contemporary form that blends movements and concepts from a variety of mind-body programs

V. List six research-supported musculoskeletal benefits of yoga and tai chi.

a. _____

b. _____

c. _____

d. _____

e. _____

f. _____

VI. Explain what is meant by "energycentric" when describing the criteria that define mind-body exercise. _____

_____

_____

_____

_____

VII. List the seven characteristics of optimal breathwork.

a. _____

b. _____

c. _____

d. _____

e. _____

f. _____

g. _____

VIII. What are the two key considerations when selecting mind-body exercise for chronic disease management?

a. _____

_____

b. _____

_____

IX. Place the 12 steps of the sun salutation in their proper order. Note that some positions and movements are used twice during the sequence.

a. _____ Breathe out, bend forward

b. _____ Breathe in, step back with the right leg

c. _____ Stand in prayer pose

d. _____ Breathe in, back slightly arched

e. _____ Breathe out, bring left foot back with the right foot

f. _____ Breathe out, assume inverted V position

g. _____ Place knees, chest, and forehead on floor

h. _____ Breathe in with upper body raised

i. _____ Breathe in, bend the right knee, and step in between the hands

j. _____ Breathe out, bring the left foot up to meet the right, bend forward

Multiple-choice Questions

1. Which of the following benefits of regular participation in mind-body exercise will have the **GREATEST** impact on improved program adherence?
    A. Increased self-efficacy
    B. Enhanced flexibility
    C. Improved muscular strength
    D. Enhanced balance

2. The affective and neuroendocrine response to mind-body exercise is mediated through the hypothalamic-pituitary-adrenal axis (HPA) and results in a decreased production of which hormones that are associated with stress?
    A. Renin and ghrelin
    B. Insulin and glucagon
    C. Catecholamines and cortisol
    D. Serotonin and acetylcholine

3. Which of the following is considered a classical form of mind-body exercise (>200-year heritage)?
    A. Tae kwon do
    B. Native American yoga
    C. Hatha yoga
    D. Feldenkrais method

4. What is a metabolic benefit of practicing yoga and tai chi on a regular basis?
    A. Increased glucose tolerance and insulin sensitivity
    B. Decreased stress hormones
    C. Increased maximum oxygen consumption
    D. Decreased resting oxygen consumption

5. What is frequently cited as the primary centering activity of mind-body exercise programs?
    A. Breathwork
    B. Kinesthetic awareness
    C. Proper choreographic form
    D. Energycentric movement

6. What is the **PRIMARY** method for progressing the principal challenge in hatha yoga?
    A. Adding an environmental challenge, such as heat
    B. Incorporating a yoga block into the patterns
    C. Adding weighted or external resistance
    D. Increasing the complexity of the asanas

7. Which of the following program modifications would be **MOST** important when teaching yoga to a client who is deconditioned or has a chronic disease?
    A. Increase breath suspensions at the end of expiration to 4–5 seconds
    B. Minimize poses with the head below the heart
    C. Avoid slow transitions from one pose to the next
    D. Increase time holding Iyengar poses for clients with hypertension

8. Which form of mind-body exercise is fundamentally a form of movement re-education that breaks inefficient movement patterns into components?
    A. Iyengar yoga
    B. Tai chi
    C. Qigong
    D. Pilates

9. Which of the following is a characteristic of mind-body exercise programs that is helpful to those with stable chronic disease?
    A. Increased real-time cognitive arousal
    B. Improved proprioception and kinesthesis
    C. Intensity levels ranging from 3–6 METs
    D. Improved aerobic capacity

10. How can a personal trainer **MOST** effectively incorporate mind-body exercise into personal-training sessions for clients?
    A. Including some Iyengar poses and yogic-breathing during the cool-down
    B. Enhancing power training through slow, controlled yogic breathing
    C. Adding yogic breathing to high-intensity intervals to facilitate greater minute ventilation ($\dot{V}_E$)
    D. Incorporating inverted poses as part of a comprehensive warm-up

Show What You Know

I. A client who has been performing aerobic exercise four days a week—alternating between treadmill jogging and using an elliptical trainer—and performing resistance exercise with free weights twice a week, tells you that he would like to incorporate some mind-body exercise into his program to provide some much-needed stress relief. He does not want to add any more time to his regimen and simply wants to add a mind-body component to his current workouts. Explain how you would introduce some mind-body techniques into this client's workouts. _____

    _____

    _____

    _____

    _____

    _____

    _____

    _____

    _____

    _____

CHAPTER 14

Exercise and Special Populations

Summary Review

An ACE-certified Personal Trainer can work with clients who have health challenges after the clients have been cleared for exercise by their personal physicians. A personal trainer who works with clients with special needs has a responsibility to expand his or her knowledge and skills in this area through continuing education and communication with healthcare professionals.

Cardiovascular Disorders

A personal trainer should understand the general characteristics of coronary artery disease (CAD), including the contributions of the following factors:
- Atherosclerosis
- Dyslipidemia
- Physical inactivity

Exercise and Coronary Artery Disease

An understanding of the following concepts as they relate to exercise and CAD is important for safe and effective exercise programming:
- The role of exercise in the treatment and prevention of CAD
- Mortality and morbidity among patients with CAD
- CAD risk factors

Exercise Guidelines

A personal trainer should have knowledge of the following concepts related to exercise programming for clients with CAD:
- Published guidelines available to assist the personal trainer in working with clients with CAD and interacting with the healthcare team
- Clinical status of the client (e.g., low risk, high risk)
- Abnormal signs or symptoms that necessitate delaying or terminating the exercise session
- Exercise recommendations for clients with cardiovascular disease

Hypertension

A personal trainer should understand the general characteristics of hypertension, including the contributions of the following factors:
- Age
- Prehypertension
- Diet
- Physical activity
- Antihypertensive medications

Exercise and Hypertension

An understanding of the following concepts as they relate to exercise and hypertension is important for safe and effective exercise programming:

- The role of exercise in the treatment and prevention of hypertension
- Average reduction in blood pressure due to regular exercise
- Magnitude of post-exercise hypotension (PEH)

Exercise Guidelines

A personal trainer should have knowledge of the following concepts related to exercise programming for clients with hypertension:

- Effect of various exercise modalities (e.g., aerobic endurance, circuit training, yoga) on hypertension
- The affects of pharmacologic therapy on the exercise response
- Abnormal signs or symptoms that necessitate delaying or terminating the exercise session
- Exercise recommendations for clients with hypertension

Stroke

A personal trainer should understand the general characteristics of stroke, including the following:

- Types of stroke (i.e., ischemic and hemorrhagic)
- Risk factors for stroke
- Disability after a stroke

A personal trainer should be aware of the warning signs of stroke.

Exercise and Stroke

An understanding of the following concepts as they relate to exercise and stroke is important for safe and effective exercise programming:

- The role of exercise in the treatment and prevention of stroke
- Impact of exercise in cardiovascular disease risk for stroke patients

Exercise Guidelines

A personal trainer should have knowledge of the following concepts related to exercise programming for clients with stroke:

- Impact of the client's neurologic deficit profile, current functional capacity, and risk-factor status on his or her ability to exercise
- Exercise recommendations for clients who have suffered a stroke

Peripheral Vascular Disease

A personal trainer should understand the general characteristics of peripheral vascular disease (PVD):

- Risk factors for PVD
- Peripheral artery occlusive disease (POAD)
- Peripheral vascular occlusive disease (PVAD)
- Claudication pain and the use of the Subjective Grading Scale for PVD

Exercise and Peripheral Vascular Disease

An understanding of the following concepts as they relate to exercise and PVD is important for safe and effective exercise programming:

- The role of exercise in the treatment and prevention of PVD
- Impact of exercise in cardiovascular disease risk for PVD patients

Exercise Guidelines

A personal trainer should have knowledge of the following concepts related to exercise programming for clients with PVD:

- The goals of an exercise program in relation to improving PVD symptoms

- The importance of client education to ease the anxiety associated with claudication pain
- Proper foot care
- Abnormal signs or symptoms that necessitate delaying or terminating the exercise session
- Exercise recommendations for clients with PVD

Dyslipidemia

A personal trainer should understand the general characteristics of dyslipidemia, including the contributions of the following factors:

- Primary lipoproteins
  - ✓ Low-density lipoprotein (LDL)
  - ✓ Very low-density lipoprotein (VLDL)
  - ✓ High-density lipoprotein (HDL)
  - ✓ Non-HDL cholesterol (non-HDL)
- Triglycerides
- 2002 National Cholesterol Education Program (NCEP) Adult Treatment Panel III (ATP III) Classification of LDL, total cholesterol, HDL cholesterol, and triglycerides
- Diet

Exercise and Dyslipidemia

An understanding of the following concepts as they relate to exercise and dyslipidemia is important for safe and effective exercise programming:

- The role of exercise in the treatment and prevention of dyslipidemia
- Average reduction in LDL and increase in HDL due to regular exercise
- The impact of body-fat decrease in the role of lipid profile improvement

Exercise Guidelines

A personal trainer should have knowledge of the following concepts related to exercise programming for clients with dyslipidemia:

- Cardiovascular disease risk factors in individuals with dyslipidemia
- Exercise recommendations for clients with dyslipidemia

Diabetes

A personal trainer should understand the general characteristics of diabetes:

- High levels of blood glucose resulting from defects in insulin production, insulin action, or both
- Manifestations of diabetes (i.e., type 1, type 2, and gestational)
- Chronic health problems associated with diabetes
- Signs and symptoms of type 1 diabetes compared with type 2 diabetes
- Benefits of exercise for individuals with type 1 diabetes
- Benefits of exercise for individuals with type 2 diabetes

Exercise Guidelines

A personal trainer should have knowledge of the following concepts related to exercise programming for clients with diabetes:

- The client's diabetes self-management program
- Carbohydrate consumption in relation to exercise blood glucose
- Exercise training recommendations for clients with type 1 or type 2 diabetes
- Complications such as autonomic and peripheral neuropathy
- Exercise precautions for clients with diabetes

Metabolic Syndrome

A personal trainer should understand the general characteristics of metabolic syndrome:

- The cluster of conditions that constitute the criteria for metabolic syndrome
- Lifestyle interventions recommended as initial strategies for the treatment of metabolic syndrome

Exercise and the Metabolic Syndrome

An understanding of the following concepts as they relate to exercise and the metabolic syndrome is important for safe and effective exercise programming:

- The role of exercise in the treatment and prevention of the metabolic syndrome
- The impact of obesity on the performance of exercise for individuals with the metabolic syndrome

Exercise Guidelines

A personal trainer should have knowledge of the following concepts related to exercise programming for clients with the metabolic syndrome:

- Strategies for increasing daily energy expenditure
- Impact of the client's weight status, overall conditioning, and medical profile on exercise intensity
- Exercise recommendations for clients with the metabolic syndrome

Asthma

A personal trainer should understand the general characteristics of asthma:

- Triggers and symptoms of asthma
- Exercise induced asthma (EIA)

Exercise and Asthma

An understanding of the following concepts as they relate to exercise and asthma is important for safe and effective exercise programming:

- The role of exercise in the prevention and treatment of asthma
- Medications used to prevent and treat asthma
- Hyperventilation

Exercise Guidelines

A personal trainer should have knowledge of the following concepts related to exercise programming for clients with asthma:

- The client's medication/treatment plan to prevent EIA attacks and a response plan to lessen the effects should an attack occur
- General activity guidelines for developing, monitoring, and progressing an exercise program for a client with asthma
- Exercise recommendations for clients with asthma

Cancer

A personal trainer should understand the general characteristics of cancer:

- Influence of age, continued population growth, and improvement in detection technology on future cancer rates
- Malignant and benign tumors
- Metastasis

Exercise and Cancer

An understanding of the following concepts as they relate to exercise and cancer is important for safe and effective exercise programming:

- The role of exercise in the prevention of certain cancers
- The role of exercise in the treatment of cancer
- The impact of chemotherapy and/or radiation treatment on exercise performance

Exercise Guidelines

A personal trainer should have knowledge of the following concepts related to exercise programming for clients with cancer:

- Numbness in the feet and/or balance problems as a result of cancer treatment that could lead to client falls
- Concerns about radiation treatment and indwelling catheters during swimming
- Exercise precautions for clients with cancer
- Exercise recommendations for clients with cancer

Osteoporosis

A personal trainer should understand the general characteristics of osteoporosis:

- Common fracture sites and the consequences of those fractures
- Osteopenia
- Bone remodeling
- Impact of lifestyle choices related to bone density

Exercise and Osteoporosis

An understanding of the following concepts as they relate to exercise and osteoporosis is important for safe and effective exercise programming:

- The role of exercise in the prevention and treatment of osteoporosis
- The importance of adequate nutrition in combination with exercise for the treatment of osteoporosis

Exercise Guidelines

A personal trainer should have knowledge of the following concepts related to exercise programming for clients with osteoporosis:

- A bone's reaction to different types of physical stress
- Strategies for preventing injuries and falls in clients with osteoporosis
- Exercise recommendations for clients with osteoporosis

Arthritis

A personal trainer should understand the general characteristics of arthritis:

- The two primary forms of arthritis (i.e., osteoarthritis and rheumatoid arthritis)
- American College of Rheumatology Revised Criteria for Classification of Functional Status in Rheumatoid Arthritis

Exercise and Arthritis

An understanding of the following concepts as they relate to exercise and arthritis is important for safe and effective exercise programming:

- The role of exercise in the prevention and treatment of arthritis
- The impact of physical inactivity in clients with arthritis

Exercise Guidelines

A personal trainer should have knowledge of the following concepts related to exercise programming for clients with arthritis:

- Effect of various exercise modalities (e.g., walking, cycling, aquatic exercise) on arthritis
- Importance of proper body alignment on exercise performance
- Exercise guidelines for individuals with a hip replacement
- Training approach when a client experiences a rheumatoid arthritis flare-up
- Training approach when a client experiences pain during and after an exercise session
- Exercise recommendations for clients with arthritis

Fibromyalgia

A personal trainer should understand the general characteristics of fibromyalgia:

- Common fibromyalgia triggers and symptoms
- 1990 American College of Rheumatology criteria for the diagnosis of fibromyalgia
- Typical treatment modalities for fibromyalgia

Exercise and Fibromyalgia

An understanding of the following concepts as they relate to exercise and fibromyalgia is important for safe and effective exercise programming:

- The role of exercise in the treatment of fibromyalgia
- The impact of physical inactivity in clients with fibromyalgia

Exercise Guidelines

A personal trainer should have knowledge of the following concepts related to exercise programming for clients with fibromyalgia:

- The role of stretching and warm-water exercise for clients with fibromyalgia
- Exercise recommendations for clients with fibromyalgia

Chronic Fatigue Syndrome

A personal trainer should understand the general characteristics of chronic fatigue syndrome (CFS):

- Common symptoms of CFS
- CFS criteria
- General treatment guidelines for CFS

Exercise Guidelines

A personal trainer should have knowledge of the following concepts related to exercise programming for clients with CFS:

- The role of exercise in the treatment of CFS
- The importance of appropriate rest following physical exertion
- Training approach if exercise worsens CFS symptoms
- Exercise recommendations for clients with CFS

Low-back Pain

A personal trainer should understand the general characteristics of low-back pain (LBP):

- Prevalence of LBP
- Typical causes of LBP

Exercise and Low-back Pain

An understanding of the following concept as it relates to exercise and LBP is important for safe and effective exercise programming:

- The role of exercise in the prevention and treatment of LBP

Exercise Guidelines

A personal trainer should have knowledge of the following concepts related to exercise programming for clients with LBP:

- Exercises or movements that clients with LBP should avoid
- Importance of neutral pelvic alignment during physical activity
- Proper lifting mechanics
- Importance of good posture
- Diurnal variation in the fluid level of the intervertebral discs
- Exercise recommendations for clients with LBP

Weight Management

A personal trainer should understand the general characteristics of lifestyle modification for weight management:

- Health consequences of overweight and obesity
- Lifestyle habits and cultural changes that contribute to weight gain and obesity

Exercise and Weight Management

An understanding of the following concept as it relates to exercise and weight management is important for safe and effective exercise programming:

- The role of exercise in the prevention and treatment of overweight and obesity

Exercise Guidelines

A personal trainer should have knowledge of the following concepts related to exercise programming for clients who are overweight or obese:

- The impact of a combination of exercise and sensible eating on weight loss
- Exercise recommendations for clients who are overweight or obese

Exercise and Older Adults

A personal trainer should understand the unique issues related to exercise and older adults, including the contributions of the following factors:

- Normal age-related changes of the cardiovascular, endocrine, respiratory, musculoskeletal, and sensory systems
- The impact of physical activity on the cognitive declines associated with aging

Exercise Guidelines

A personal trainer should have knowledge of the following concepts related to exercise programming for older clients:

- The role of exercise in delaying the physiological declines associated with aging
- The importance of exercises intended to maintain or improve balance
- The impact of physical activity on common chronic health problems experienced by older adults
- Exercise recommendations for older adults

Exercise and Youth

A personal trainer should understand the unique issues related to exercise and youth:

- Prevalence and health consequences of physical inactivity among youth
- Health consequences related to poor nutrition habits among youth

Exercise Guidelines

A personal trainer should have knowledge of the following concepts related to exercise programming for youth:

- The health benefits associated with regular physical activity in youth
- Guidelines to minimize the risk of injury during resistance training in youth
- The impact of environmental temperature extremes in exercising youth
- Guidelines for working effectively with youth at different stages of physical and psychological development
- Exercise recommendations for youth

Pre- and Postnatal Exercise

A personal trainer should understand the unique issues related to exercise and the pre- and postnatal client:

- Evidence in support of the safety of exercise and physical activity during pregnancy and the postpartum period

- Common physiological changes during pregnancy that affect a woman's ability to exercise

Exercise Guidelines for Pregnant Women

A personal trainer should have knowledge of the following concepts related to exercise programming for pregnant clients:
- Published guidelines for exercise during pregnancy and the postpartum period
- Health conditions that preclude pregnant women from exercising
- Contraindicated exercises for pregnant women
- Abnormal signs or symptoms that necessitate delaying or terminating the exercise session
- Exercise recommendations for pregnancy and the postpartum period

Getting Started

This chapter describes a variety of client health concerns that a personal trainer is likely to encounter, and provides exercise guidelines and a sample exercise recommendation for each. Guidelines for working with youth, older adults, and pregnant women are also discussed. After completing this chapter, you will have a better understanding of:
- The following diseases and disorders: coronary artery disease, hypertension, stroke, peripheral vascular disease, dyslipidemia, diabetes, metabolic syndrome, asthma, cancer, osteoporosis, arthritis, fibromyalgia, chronic fatigue syndrome, low-back pain, and overweight and obesity
- The prevalence of each disease or disorder
- How the body's response to exercise is affected by each disease or disorder
- Specific contraindications for exercise associated with each disease or disorder

Reading Assignment

Read Chapter 14 of the *ACE Personal Trainer Manual*, 4th edition, paying special attention to the boldface terms in the chapter. After you have read the chapter, define those terms on a separate piece of paper.

Expand Your Knowledge

I. According to the Centers for Disease Control and Prevention, a reduction in what three factors would dramatically reduce the incidence of chronic disease?

   a. _____

   b. _____

   c. _____

II. Fill in the blanks.

   a. An ACE-certified Personal Trainer is certified to work with clients that have health challenges only after they _____.

   b. _____ is characterized by abdominal obesity, atherogenic dyslipidemia, elevated blood pressure, insulin resistance, prothrombotic state, and proinflammatory state.

   c. _____ cells typically metastasize, while _____ cells stay locally at the site of origin and do not spread throughout the body.

   d. Many cancer patients are at increased risk of developing _____ due to treatment side effects combined with inactivity during treatment. Thus, _____ is an appropriate first step in the cardiovascular recovery phase for most cancer clients.

III. Consider the effect of aging on the following variables. Place an (I) next to the variables that tend to increase during the aging process, a (D) next to those that decrease, and an (NC) next to those that do not change.

   a. _____ Maximal heart rate

   b. _____ Body-fat percentage

   c. _____ Maximum oxygen uptake

   d. _____ Basal metabolic rate

   e. _____ Coordination

IV. Which of the following three types of exercise programs would you recommend for an obese client who wants to lose weight? Explain why you would recommend that program.

   a. Aerobic endurance only

   b. Strength training only

   c. A combination of aerobic endurance and strength training

   _____

   _____

   _____

   _____

   _____

V. Match the health concern to the appropriate exercise recommendation. In some cases, the exercise recommendation may apply to more than one health concern.

1. Extend the warm-up and cool-down periods

2. In some cases, avoid upper-body exercises

3. Avoid extreme environmental conditions (high or low temperature)

4. Avoid forward-head positions in which the chin is tilted up

5. Use isometric strengthening exercises

a. _____ Low-back pain

b. _____ Arthritis

c. _____ Osteoporosis

d. _____ Asthma

VI. List the types of movements that clients diagnosed with lower-back pain should avoid.

_____

_____

_____

_____

_____

_____

VII. List the exercise guidelines for a low-risk client with stable cardiovascular artery disease who is initiating an exercise program.

a. Mode _____

_____

_____

b. Intensity _____

_____

_____

c. Duration _____

_____

_____

d. Frequency _____

_____

_____

VIII. Match the health concern to the appropriate exercise recommendations.

1. Exercise at the same time each day for better control

2. Avoid holding breath or straining during exercise (Valsalva maneuver)

3. Avoid exercising in cold air or water to reduce the risk of vasoconstriction

4. Give special attention to foot care and hygiene

5. No heavy lifting; keep resistance low to moderate and repetitions high

6. Move slowly when changing positions

a. _____ Hypertension

b. _____ Peripheral vascular disease

c. _____ Diabetes

IX. Explain the major differences between the following pairs of words or phrases.

a. Osteoarthritis and rheumatoid arthritis _____

_____

_____

b. Type 1 diabetes and type 2 diabetes _____

_____

_____

c. Ischemic stroke and hemorrhagic stroke _____

_____

_____

d. Low-density lipoprotein (LDL) and high-density lipoprotein (HDL) _____

_____

_____

e. Fibromyalgia and chronic fatigue syndrome _____

_____

_____

X. List the types of activities that clients with osteoporosis should avoid. _____

_____

_____

_____

_____

XI. List the five warning signs of stroke of which a personal trainer must be aware.

a. _____

b. _____

c. _____

d. _____

e. _____

Multiple-choice Questions

1. You are working with a client who has osteoarthritis. He shows up to his latest session and tells you that he has been "experiencing soreness in his right knee since helping his daughter move into a new apartment over the weekend." In which section of this client's SOAP notes should this information be recorded?
   A. Subjective
   B. Objective
   C. Assessment
   D. Plan

2. You are working with a client who has hypertension and has been cleared by her physician for exercise. Which of the following would be **MOST** appropriate for her initial resistance-training program?
   A. Mostly bodyweight exercises with isometric contractions held initially for 10–15 seconds, working up to 30 seconds
   B. Two sets of 8–12 repetitions on 8–10 exercises addressing all major muscle groups using mostly cables and dumbbells at an intensity of 70–80% 1 RM
   C. One set of 6–8 repetitions performed on 8–10 selectorized machines to address all major muscle groups at an intensity of 80–85% 1 RM
   D. Circuit training consisting of 8–10 exercises using mostly tubing and bodyweight performed one time for 12–16 repetitions at 60–70% 1 RM

3. What effect does regular exercise have on dyslipidemia?
   A. Exercise alone will significantly reduce total cholesterol levels
   B. Regular exercise can increase LDL levels
   C. Triglyceride levels are reduced for up to 12 hours following exercise
   D. Regular exercise can increase HDL levels

4. You are working with a client who has type 1 diabetes and checks his blood glucose levels prior to each exercise session. Which of the following pre-exercise blood glucose levels would make you postpone the exercise session until his blood sugar is under control?
   A. 88 mg/dL
   B. 110 mg/dL
   C. 155 mg/dL
   D. 215 mg/dL

5. You are designing an exercise program for a new client who has type 2 diabetes and a physician's release for exercise as tolerated to lose weight and improve blood glucose regulation. During the initial session, you learn that she has been sedentary for the past few years. What initial cardiorespiratory program would be most appropriate for her?
   A. Walking 5–6 days per week for 40 minutes at an RPE of 11–13, working up to 60 minutes
   B. Cycling 3–4 days per week for 40 minutes at an RPE of 13–15, working up to 60 minutes
   C. Walking 5–6 days per week for 10–20 minutes at an RPE of 11–13, working up to 40–60 minutes
   D. Cycling 3–4 days per week for 10–20 minutes at an RPE of 13–15, working up to 40–60 minutes

6. Which of the clients described below meets the criteria for the metabolic syndrome?

   A. 33-year-old male:
      Waist circumference = 36 in (91.4 cm)
      Triglycerides = 188 mg/dL
      HDL cholesterol = 43 mg/dL
      Blood pressure = 130/82 mmHg
      Fasting blood glucose = 112 mg/dL

   B. 42-year-old female:
      Waist circumference = 36 in (91.4 cm)
      Triglycerides = 133 mg/dL
      HDL cholesterol = 47 mg/dL
      Blood pressure = 128/87 mmHg
      Fasting blood glucose = 107 mg/dL

   C. 48-year-old male:
      Waist circumference = 43 in (109.2 cm)
      Triglycerides = 125 mg/dL
      HDL cholesterol = 44 mg/dL
      Blood pressure = 137/88 mmHg
      Fasting blood glucose = 91 mg/dL

   D. 51-year-old female:
      Waist circumference = 33 in (83.8 cm)
      Triglycerides = 172 mg/dL
      HDL cholesterol = 54 mg/dL
      Blood pressure = 127/79 mmHg
      Fasting blood glucose = 98 mg/dL

7. Which of the following steps would be **MOST** appropriate for personal trainers to take to reduce the risk of exercise-induced asthma (EIA) episodes when working with clients who have asthma?

   A. Have clients with asthma use additional inhaler medication prior to all exercise sessions
   B. Keep exercise intensities low-to-moderate for all clients with asthma
   C. Include an extended warm-up and cool-down
   D. Perform exercise sessions outside on hot, dry days

8. Which of the following repetition ranges is recommended to stimulate bone changes in clients who have osteopenia and/or osteoporosis?

   A. 6–8
   B. 10–12
   C. 12–16
   D. 15–20

9. Which of the following progressions is **LEAST** recommended for clients who have osteoarthritis?

   A. Emphasizing body alignment and exercise techniques at all times
   B. Increasing the weight lifted instead of increasing the number of repetitions
   C. Utilizing a variety of low-impact activities to avoid overstressing the joints
   D. Increasing exercise duration instead of increasing exercise intensity

10. Which of the following statements is **CORRECT** regarding exercise for people who have low-back pain?

    A. Developing low-back strength is more important for long-term back health than developing low-back endurance
    B. Low-back exercises have the most beneficial effect when performed on a daily basis
    C. Full-ROM spinal movements with an external load are best performed shortly after rising from bed
    D. Supine double-leg raises should be avoided, but prone double-leg raises are beneficial for clients who have low-back pain

Show What You Know

I.   Describe how you would gradually reduce the intensity, duration, and frequency of a pregnant client's workout that consisted of high-impact aerobics three times per week and cycling outdoors 20 miles/day (75 minutes) two days per week.

a. First trimester: _____

_____

b. Second trimester: _____

_____

c. Third trimester: _____

_____

II. You have taken on a new client, Ima Young, who is an 11-year-old girl. Her parents hired you because the physical education program at her school has been dropped. Describe the general recommendations you would make for Ima in the following areas.

a. Mode _____

_____

b. Intensity _____

_____

c. Duration _____

_____

d. Frequency _____

_____

e. Strength training _____

_____

CHAPTER 15

Common Musculoskeletal Injuries and Implications for Exercise

Summary Review

Types of Tissue and Common Tissue Injuries

Personal trainers should have a basic understanding of the following musculoskeletal injuries and their impact on a client's exercise performance:

- Muscle strains and tendinitis
- Ligament sprains
- Common overuse conditions
- Cartilage damage
- Bone fractures

Tissue Reaction to Healing

A personal trainer should understand the following three phases of systematic healing, as well as the signs and symptoms of inflammation:

- Inflammatory phase
- Fibroblastic/proliferation phase
- Maturation/remodeling phase

Musculoskeletal Injuries

Personal trainers should have a basic understanding of the following concepts related to musculoskeletal injuries and their impact on a client's exercise performance:

- Pre-existing injuries
- Program modification
- Acute injury management
- Flexibility and musculoskeletal injuries

Upper-extremity Injuries

Personal trainers should have a basic understanding of the signs and symptoms, management, and exercise programming guidelines for the following upper-extremity musculoskeletal injuries and their impact on a client's exercise performance:

- Rotator cuff injuries
- Elbow tendinitis
- Carpal tunnel syndrome

Low-back Pain

Personal trainers should have a basic understanding of the following concepts related to low-back pain and their impact on a client's exercise performance:

- Common risk factors associated with low-back pain
- Causes of low-back pain
  ✓ Mechanical pain
  ✓ Degenerative disc disease and sciatica

Lower-extremity Injuries

Personal trainers should have a basic understanding of the signs and symptoms, management, and exercise programming guidelines for the following lower-extremity musculoskeletal injuries and their impact on a client's exercise performance:

- Greater trochanteric bursitis
- Iliotibial band syndrome
- Patellofemoral pain syndrome
- Infrapatellar tendinitis
- Shin splints
- Ankle sprains
- Achilles tendinitis
- Plantar fasciitis

Record Keeping

A personal trainer should understand the following principles related to appropriate record keeping for his or her client:

- Obtaining a medical history for each client
- Maintaining an exercise record for each client
- Completing and filing an incident report
- Corresponding with other healthcare professionals

Getting Started

This chapter describes how to develop programs for clients with pre-existing musculoskeletal injuries in order to minimize the risk of further injury. This chapter begins by describing the various types of tissue and tissue injury, before detailing specific injuries of the upper and lower extremities. After completing this chapter, you will have a better understanding of:

- The signs and symptoms of inflammation
- The relationship between flexibility and musculoskeletal injuries
- The following upper-extremity injuries: shoulder strain/sprain, rotator cuff injuries, elbow tendinitis, and carpal tunnel syndrome
- The following lower-extremity injuries: greater trochanteric bursitis, iliotibial band syndrome, patellofemoral pain syndrome, infrapatellar tendinitis, shin splints, ankle sprains, Achilles tendinitis, and plantar fasciitis
- The causes of low-back pain
- The importance of proper and thorough record-keeping procedures

Reading Assignment

Read Chapter 15 of the *ACE Personal Trainer Manual,* 4th edition, paying special attention to the boldface terms in the chapter. After you have read the chapter, define those terms on a separate piece of paper.

Expand Your Knowledge

I. Fill in the blanks.

   a. Muscle _____ are injuries in which the muscle works beyond its capacity, resulting in microscopic tears of the muscle fibers.

   b. Ligament _____ often, but not always, occur with trauma, such as a fall, or during contact sports.

   c. The most commonly reported knee injury is damage to the _____.

   d. The most commonly cited causes of low-back pain are _____, _____, and _____.

II. List four risk factors for muscle strains.

   a. _____

   b. _____

   c. _____

   d. _____

III. List the typical treatment options for each grade of ligament sprain.

   a. Grade I (minimal impairment) _____

   _____

   _____

   _____

   b. Grade II (moderate impairment) _____

   _____

   _____

   _____

   c. Grade III (severe impairment) _____

   _____

   _____

   _____

IV. Match each injury with the appropriate mechanism of injury or possible risk factors.

   1. Risk factors: Improper training methods, sudden changes in training surface, lower-extremity muscle weakness and/or tightness, foot overpronation

   2. Risk factors: poor flexibility, poor posture, muscle imbalance, improper warm-up, training errors

   3. Mechanism of injury: impact on the outer knee with no twisting involved

   4. Mechanism of injury: deceleration of the body combined with a maneuver of twisting, pivoting, or side-stepping

   a. _____ Hamstring strain

   b. _____ ACL injury

   c. _____ MCL injury

   d. _____ Chondromalacia

Common Musculoskeletal Injuries and Implications for Exercise

V. Match each overuse injury with the areas of the body where it is most commonly diagnosed.

1. Shoulders, hips, and knees

2. Shoulders, elbows, knees, and ankles

3. Bottom and back of the foot

a. _____ Tendinitis

b. _____ Bursitis

c. _____ Fasciitis

VI. List and describe the three phases of the tissue healing process.

a. _____

_____

_____

b. _____

_____

_____

c. _____

_____

_____

VII. What are the five signs and symptoms of tissue inflammation? _____

_____

_____

VIII. What is the most important question that a personal trainer must be able to answer about every client? _____

_____

_____

IX. What are the five components of the P.R.I.C.E. acronym?

P = _____

R = _____

I = _____

C = _____

E = _____

X. List the relative and absolute contraindications to stretching that a personal trainer must consider to prevent injury.

a. Relative contraindications _____

_____

_____

b. Absolute contraindications _____

_____

_____

XI. Match the following upper-extremity injuries with their common signs and symptoms.

1. Nagging pain during aggravating injuries (e.g., shaking hands, turning door knobs)

2. Local pain at the shoulder that radiates down the arm

3. A sudden "tearing" sensation followed by immediate pain and loss of motion

4. Pain, weakness, or numbness in the radial three-and-a-half digits of the hand and the palmar aspect of the thumb

a. _____ Shoulder strain/sprain

b. _____ Rotator cuff tear

c. _____ Elbow tendinitis

d. _____ Carpal tunnel syndrome

XII. Match the following upper-extremity injuries with aggravating activities or movements.

1. Overhead activities; lifting of heavy objects

2. Overhead and across-the-body movements; any movements that involve placing the hand behind the back

3. Full wrist flexion or extension

4. Repetitive elbow and wrist flexion and extension

a. _____ Shoulder strain/sprain

b. _____ Rotator cuff tear

c. _____ Elbow tendinitis

d. _____ Carpal tunnel syndrome

XIII. List nine risk factors associated with low-back pain.

a. _____

b. _____

c. _____

d. _____

e. _____

f. _____

g. _____

h. _____

i. _____

XIV. Match each of these lower-body musculoskeletal injuries with the appropriate exercise programming tip or guideline.

1. The exercise program should emphasize regaining strength and flexibility of the wrist, elbow, and finger flexors and extensors.

2. The exercise program should emphasize regaining strength and flexibility in the shoulder complex.

3. Restoring proper proprioception, flexibility, and strength is key, as there may be a loss of balance.

4. The goal should be to continue what was done in physical therapy in a safe, progressive manner; performing overhead activities or keeping the arm straight during exercise should be limited.

a. _____	Shoulder sprain/strain
b. _____	Rotator cuff injury
c. _____	Elbow tendinitis
d. _____	Carpal tunnel syndrome
e. _____	Greater trochanteric bursitis
f. _____	Iliotibial band syndrome
g. _____	Patellofemoral pain syndrome
h. _____	Infrapatellar tendinitis
i. _____	Shin splints
j. _____	Ankle sprains
k. _____	Achilles tendinitis
l. _____	Plantar fasciitis

5. Exercise should focus on restoring proper strength throughout the hip, knee, and ankle. Closed-chain exercises such as squats and lunges may be beneficial.

6. The exercise program should emphasize regaining strength and flexibility at the hip and lateral thigh.

7. Regaining strength and flexibility of the flexor/pronator and extensor/supinator muscle groups of the wrist and elbow is important.

8. Restoring proper length to the calf muscles can reduce strain to the muscle-tendon unit and decrease symptoms.

9. Cross-training to maintain adequate levels of fitness is indicated in the early stages, as is a general lower-body stretching program.

10. The exercise program should emphasize regaining strength and flexibility at the hip.

11. Exercise should focus on restoring proper strength throughout the hip, knee, and ankle and proper flexibility in the iliotibial band, hamstrings, and calves.

12. The goal is to design a program that challenges the client but does not excessively load the foot.

XV. List five guidelines that personal trainers can share with clients regarding how to purchase appropriate footwear for exercise.

a. _____

b. _____

c. _____

d. _____

e. _____

Multiple-choice Questions

1. Which of the following would be contraindicated for a client who has an acute hamstring strain?
    A. Educating the client about using P.R.I.C.E. as an early intervention strategy
    B. Modifying the workout focusing on the non-injured points of the body
    C. Stretching the hamstrings for up to 60 seconds per stretch
    D. Recommending that the client see a physician if pain persists

2. Where is the scapular plane?
    A. In line with the frontal plane
    B. 30 degrees lateral to the sagittal plane
    C. In line with the sagittal plane
    D. 30 degrees anterior to the frontal plane

3. An inflammation of the wrist extensors near their origin is commonly referred to as
    _____.
    A. Medial epicondylitis
    B. Tennis elbow
    C. Golfer's elbow
    D. Olecranon bursitis

4. Which nerve is commonly compressed due to carpal tunnel syndrome?
    A. Median nerve
    B. Ulnar nerve
    C. Radial nerve
    D. Musculocutaneous nerve

5. Clients returning to exercise following greater trochanteric bursitis should generally avoid
    _____.
    A. Prone exercise positions that press on the anterior superior iliac spines
    B. Stretching the iliotibial (IT) band complex
    C. Side-lying exercise positions that compress the lateral hip
    D. Strengthening the deep hip rotator muscles

6. When working with a client who has a history of iliotibial (IT) band syndrome, which muscle group acting on the hip joint is **MOST** likely to be weak?
    A. Hip flexors
    B. Hip extensors
    C. Hip adductors
    D. Hip abductors

7. Tightness in which of the following structures can be a cause of patellofemoral pain syndrome due to its lateral fascial connections to the patella?
    A. IT band complex
    B. Hamstrings
    C. Peroneus longus
    D. Biceps femoris

8. Stretching which muscles has been shown to help relieve symptoms associated with medial tibial stress syndrome (MTSS) and/or anterior shin splints?
    A. Gastrocnemius, soleus, and peroneal group
    B. Soleus and anterior compartment of the lower leg
    C. Tibialis anterior and plantar fascia
    D. Tibialis posterior and lateral compartment

9. What exercises would be **MOST** important to include for a client who has recovered from Achilles tendinitis and wants to prevent it from returning?
    A. Eccentric strengthening for the calf complex through controlled plantarflexion against gravity and stretching the calf muscles
    B. High-intensity strength training for the calf complex and stretching of the flexor hallucis longus and tibialis posterior
    C. Eccentric strengthening for the calf complex through controlled dorsiflexion against gravity and stretching the calf muscles
    D. Comprehensive stretching and isometric strength-training program for the muscles of the lower limb

10. When working with a client who has a history of plantar fasciitis, it would be **MOST** important to included stretching exercises for the _____.
    A. Gastrocnemius, soleus, and plantar fascia
    B. Plantar fascia, peroneus longus, and peroneus brevis
    C. Gastrocnemius, tibialis posterior, and tibialis anterior
    D. Plantar fascia, tibialis anterior, and flexor digitorum longus

Show What You Know

I. A client with iliotibial band syndrome begins running on sand after reading in a magazine that doing so would reduce her risk of injury as compared to running on the track at the local high school. Since making the change, she has begun experiencing some tightness in her ankles, specifically in the Achilles tendon area. Explain to this client why she may be experiencing this new pain and what she can do to protect her lower extremities when running on sand. _____

    _____

    _____

    _____

    _____

    _____

    _____

    _____

    _____

II. Explain how you would modify the following exercises for the specific client described.

    a. Overhead press for a client with a shoulder strain _____

    _____

    _____

    b. Straight-arm front raise for a client with rotator cuff injury _____

    _____

    _____

    c. Squats for a client with iliotibial band syndrome _____

    _____

    _____

    d. Leg extensions for a client with patellofemoral pain syndrome _____

    _____

    _____

CHAPTER 16
Emergency Procedures

Summary Review

Personal trainers should have a systematic approach for handling various types of emergency situations and have knowledge of concepts related to the following emergency-specific factors:

- Personal protective equipment
- Scene safety
- Maintaining a first-aid kit
- Emergency policies and procedures for fitness facilities
- Record keeping and confidentiality
  - ✓ Health Insurance Portability and Accountability Act (HIPAA)
- Emergency assessment
  - ✓ Primary assessment
  - ✓ Secondary assessment
- Activating EMS
  - ✓ When to call 9-1-1
  - ✓ Land lines vs. cell phones
  - ✓ Emergency call centers
- Initial response
  - ✓ Cardiopulmonary resuscitation (CPR)
  - ✓ Automated external defibrillation (AED)

Common Medical Emergencies and Injuries

Personal trainers should have basic knowledge of the following common medical emergencies and injuries, the signs and symptoms of each, and recommended treatments:

- Dyspnea
- Choking
- Asthma
- Cardiovascular disease, chest pain, and heart attack
- Syncope
- Stroke
- Insulin reaction (hypoglycemia)
- Heat illness
- Cold illness
- Seizures
- Soft-tissue injuries
- Fractures
- Head injuries
- Neck and back injuries
- Shock

Universal Precautions and Protection Against Bloodborne Pathogens

Due to the threat of communicable disease, personal trainers should understand universal precautions when dealing with bloodborne pathogens, specifically hepatitis B and C and HIV.

Getting Started

This chapter describes most of the common medical emergencies that personal trainers might encounter, as well as appropriate procedures for responding to them. After completing this chapter, you will have a better understanding of:

- The various types of emergency equipment and emergency medical services
- The steps for primary and secondary assessment
- The ABCs of basic life support
- The symptoms of common medical emergencies and injuries
- Practices that may prevent medical emergencies
- Bloodborne pathogens and how to avoid exposure
- Cardiopulmonary resuscitation and automated external defibrillation

Reading Assignment

Read Chapter 16 of the *ACE Personal Trainer Manual,* 4th edition, paying special attention to the boldface terms in the chapter. After you have read the chapter, define those terms on a separate piece of paper.

Expand Your Knowledge

I.   How can the use of the Physical Activity Readiness Questionnaire (PAR-Q) help
      prevent an emergency situation? _____

      _____

      _____

      _____

      _____

      _____

II.   What five pieces of information must be included on the incident report following an
      emergency?

      a. _____

      b. _____

      c. _____

      d. _____

      e. _____

III. Define the four components of the ABCs used as part of the primary assessment to
      determine if an emergency is life-threatening.

      A = _____

      B = _____

      C = _____

      s = _____

IV.   Answer the following questions about the primary assessment of an emergency incident.
      a. If a victim is unable to give consent to receive help because he or she is unresponsive
          or disoriented, how should the personal trainer proceed? _____

          _____

          _____

      b. Explain how to perform the chin-lift maneuver for opening the victim's airway. _____

          _____

          _____

      c. What should the personal trainer do if an assessment of the victim's breathing reveals
          that it is gasping or irregular? _____

          _____

          _____

      d. What is the next step if the initial assessment of the victim's circulation has found no
          pulse? _____

          _____

          _____

V.   Answer the following questions about the secondary assessment of an emergency incident.
     a. What is the purpose of the secondary assessment? _____

     _____

     _____

     b. What are the two possible indicators that it is time to move into the secondary
         assessment of a victim? _____

     _____

     _____

     c. What can a quick check of skin color and temperature reveal about the victim's
         general health? _____

     _____

     _____

VI. When is it appropriate to call 9-1-1? _____

     _____

     _____

VII. Place an X beside each situation if it would be appropriate to call 9-1-1 or activate the
     EMS system.

     a. _____ A client has a seizure

     b. _____ A client breaks his or her femur

     c. _____ A client suddenly cannot move a part of his or her body

     d. _____ A client is having trouble breathing

     e. _____ A carbon monoxide alarm is activated

     f. _____ A trainer wants to check on the status of an ongoing emergency

VIII. List seven questions that a caller must be ready to answer when calling 9-1-1 to report
      an emergency.

     a. _____

     b. _____

     c. _____

     d. _____

     e. _____

     f. _____

     g. _____

IX. List the four steps in the AHA's Chain of Survival.

     a. _____

     b. _____

     c. _____

     d. _____

X. Explain "hands-only CPR," defining for whom it might be effective and why. _____

_____

_____

_____

_____

_____

XI. Describe the initial signs and symptoms of each of the following common medical emergencies.

a. Heart attack _____

_____

_____

_____

_____

b. Stroke affecting the right side of the brain _____

_____

_____

_____

c. Hypoglycemia _____

_____

_____

d. Tonic clonic seizure _____

_____

_____

_____

_____

e. Shock _____

_____

_____

XII. How should a personal trainer care for a victim of heat stroke? _____

_____

_____

_____

_____

XIII. List the emergency procedures for a generalized tonic clonic seizure.

    a. _____

    b. _____

    c. _____

    d. _____

XIV. List 15 warning signs that personal trainers must be aware of when monitoring an individual following a possible concussion.

    a. _____

    b. _____

    c. _____

    d. _____

    e. _____

    f. _____

    g. _____

    h. _____

    i. _____

    j. _____

    k. _____

    l. _____

    m. _____

    n. _____

    o. _____

XV. What are the universal precautions that a rescuer can use to stay protected from bloodborne pathogens? _____

_____

_____

_____

XVI. List the four components of the RICE acronym and explain the role of each in the treatment of soft-tissue injuries.

    R= _____

_____

    I= _____

_____

    C= _____

_____

    E= _____

_____

Multiple-choice Questions

1. What is the **MOST** important step a fitness facility can take to minimize risks of cardiovascular events?
    A. Having each member complete a release of liability waiver and informed consent
    B. Requiring all members to have physical examinations before beginning exercise programs
    C. Having each member complete a medical history form
    D. Requiring all members to start programs at a low-to-moderate intensity

2. Which of the following **CORRECTLY** describes the Health Insurance Portability and Accountability Act (HIPAA) of 1996?
    A. It ensures individual privacy by requiring confidentiality of health documents
    B. It requires an individual to share health information with his or her physician
    C. It requires an individual to share health information with his or her insurance agency
    D. It ensures that individual health records are accessible at all times via an electronic database

3. What should you do **FIRST** with a person who suddenly falls to the floor while exercising?
    A. Ask the person what led to the injury
    B. Check for any medical jewelry to determine the cause of the condition
    C. Assess the person's pulse and blood pressure
    D. Assess if the person is conscious and asking if he or she is okay

4. What is the **PRIMARY** reason people give for not attempting CPR in a cardiac emergency?
    A. Fear of lawsuits due to cracked ribs
    B. Uncertainty about their ability to perform CPR correctly
    C. Fear of performing CPR when it is not needed
    D. Uncomfortable with putting their mouth on a stranger

5. What is the **MOST** common heart rhythm during cardiac arrest?
    A. Atrial fibrillation
    B. Atrial bradycardia
    C. Ventricular fibrillation
    D. Ventricular tachycardia

6. A heart attack is characterized by which of the following signs and symptoms?
    A. A sudden, severe headache and weakness on one side of the body
    B. Sustained stabbing pain in and around the chest
    C. Sudden loss of consciousness, with no breathing and no pulse
    D. A squeezing pressure in the chest that can be mistaken for heart burn

7. How is a transient ischemic attack (TIA) different from a stroke?
    A. A TIA is caused by a different physiological mechanism
    B. A stroke is not treatable, but a TIA is
    C. Signs of a TIA last less than one hour
    D. A TIA feels less severe and is less frightening than a stroke

8. Which of the following are actions to take when you suspect a client is having a mild hypoglycemic incident?
    A. Help the client sit down and give him a sugary drink if he can swallow
    B. Call EMS rescuers, start the steps of CPR, and get an available AED
    C. Help the client sit down and give him insulin if he has it available
    D. Immediately call for EMS rescuers to respond and monitor the person

9. Which of the following is a critical indicator that someone is suffering from heat stroke and in need of emergency treatment?
    A. Increased body temperature
    B. Altered mental status
    C. Red hot, sweaty skin
    D. Fatigue, weakness, and headache

10. Which treatment of soft-tissue injuries is within the personal trainer scope of practice?
    A. Recommending that the client take NSAIDs (non-steroidal anti inflammatory drugs)
    B. Performing massage on the affected soft tissue
    C. Administering ultrasound to the affected soft tissue
    D. Educating the client on the proper administration of ice using the P.R.I.C.E. principle

Show What You Know

I.   In the following cases, identify the common medical emergency or injury and outline your response.

a.   You are training a client, Tip Hoever, when 45 minutes into the session you begin to notice that he is starting to act as if he is under the influence of alcohol. He is trembling and has slurred speech and poor coordination. Tip complains that he is tired and has a severe headache. As he attempts to sit down, Tip falls backward and is lying on the floor unconscious. _____

_____

_____

_____

_____

_____

_____

b. You are about to meet your client for a training session when you notice that he is stretching his calf muscle by placing one leg behind the other and pushing on a wall. On second glance, you notice that your client is actually pushing on a large window. As you walk over to warn him, the glass gives way and your client receives multiple cuts to his hands and wrists. As he turns, he holds up his wrists and appears panicked. He is bleeding profusely from his wrists and blood gets on your hands, face, and clothes.

_____

_____

_____

_____

_____

_____

Practice What You Know

Write out an action plan for the medical emergencies and injuries that you are likely to encounter in your daily work. You can use the information as a reference, to role play, or to review as needed. _____

_____

_____

_____

_____

_____

CHAPTER 17

Legal Guidelines and Professional Responsibilities

Summary Review

To achieve professional success, personal trainers must have knowledge regarding the following business- and legal-related concepts and their impact on the professional environment:

- Business structure
  - ✓ Sole proprietorships
  - ✓ Partnerships
  - ✓ Corporations
  - ✓ Independent contractors
  - ✓ Employees
- Contracts
  - ✓ Agreements to participate
  - ✓ Informed consent
  - ✓ Waivers
- Insurance
  - ✓ Liability insurance
- Scope of practice
- Legal responsibilities
  - ✓ Negligence
  - ✓ Vicarious liability
  - ✓ Facilities
  - ✓ Equipment
  - ✓ Supervision
  - ✓ Instruction
  - ✓ Safety guidelines
- Other business concerns with legal implications
  - ✓ Marketing activities
  - ✓ Intellectual property
  - ✓ Proper use of the ACE name and logo
  - ✓ Transportation
  - ✓ Financing
- Risk management
  - ✓ Risk identification
  - ✓ Risk evaluation
  - ✓ Selection of an approach for managing each risk
  - ✓ Implementation
  - ✓ Evaluation

Getting Started

This chapter is designed to increase your comfort level with the legal issues related to personal training and address some of the legal and business concerns you may have as a personal trainer. After completing this chapter, you will have a better understanding of:

- The legal responsibilities of a personal trainer
- The differences between independent contractors and employees
- The elements of a binding contract
- The types of business structures available to personal trainers, as well as the advantages and disadvantages of each
- Basic legal concepts and defenses

Reading Assignment

Read Chapter 17 of the *ACE Personal Trainer Manual*, 4th edition, paying special attention to the boldface terms in the chapter. After you have read the chapter, define those terms on a separate piece of paper.

Expand Your Knowledge

I.   Answer the following questions about business partnerships.

a. Why would most attorneys advise against operating a business with a 50-50 partnership? _____

_____

_____

b. Why might the minority partner in a 60-40 partnership be less likely to invest as much money as he or she might if given operating control? _____

_____

_____

c. Why are partnerships in which one partner does the "hands-on" training while the other coordinates the "office" activities particularly prone to problems? _____

_____

_____

II.   Describe the major differences between the following pairs of words or phrases.

a. Express partnership and implied partnership _____

_____

_____

b. General partner and limited partner _____

_____

_____

c. S-corp and C-corp _____

_____

_____

d. Flow-through taxation and double taxation _____

_____

_____

III. Fill in this chart by listing the advantages and disadvantages of each type of business structure.

Type	Advantage	Disadvantage
Sole proprietorship		
Partnership		
S-corps		
LLC/LLP		
C-corps		

IV. Explain the four primary disadvantages of owning and operating a fitness franchise.

a. _____

_____

_____

b. _____

_____

_____

c. _____

_____

_____

d. _____

_____

_____

V. List the eight criteria that courts have used to determine cases in which the designation of an individual as an employee or independent contractor has come into question.

a. _____

b. _____

c. _____

d. _____

e. _____

f. _____

g. _____

h. _____

VI. Place (E) beside each item that describes an employee and (IC) beside each item that describes an independent contractor.
    a. _____ Chooses when and where to work
    b. _____ Receives regularly scheduled payments
    c. _____ Charges variable fees in different situations
    d. _____ Performs work integral to the core function of a business
    e. _____ Is hired with an open-ended agreement
    f. _____ Begins working without extensive guidance
    g. _____ Maintains autonomy in training situations
    h. _____ Typically works for only one facility

VII. List the four items necessary to form a binding contract.

    a. _____

    b. _____

    c. _____

    d. _____

VIII. Describe the major differences between the following pairs of words or phrases.
    a. Act of omission and act of commission _____

    _____

    _____

    b. Contributory negligence and comparative negligence _____

    _____

    _____

    c. General supervision and specific supervision _____

    _____

    _____

    d. Umbrella liability and vicarious liability _____

    _____

    _____

IX. Select the statements that fall within the scope of practice of a personal trainer by marking them with an (X).
    a. _____ Using a health-history form to prescribe treatment
    b. _____ Understanding a client's stress is due to a recent marital dispute
    c. _____ Recommending that your seemingly healthy client run for cardiovascular benefits
    d. _____ Advising your client to take antioxidants

Legal Guidelines and Professional Responsibilities

X. For each of the following situations, describe how you could lower your risk of being found legally responsible if an injury occurred.

a. When a client complains that her new shoes hurt her feet, you say, "It takes a couple of workouts to break in a good pair of shoes." _____

_____

_____

_____

b. While personal training at a health club, you notice that the clamps that keep the weights on the barbell are getting rusty and loose. You mention their condition to the fitness director, but continue to use them. _____

_____

_____

_____

c. You are about to begin a 5-mile jog with a client when the client invites a neighbor to join you. The neighbor is not your client. _____

_____

_____

_____

d. You receive new business cards stating that you are a certified personal trainer and that you provide exercise prescriptions. _____

_____

_____

_____

XI. List five issues that must be considered during the inspection of a fitness facility.

a. _____

_____

b. _____

_____

c. _____

_____

d. _____

_____

XII. List the five steps of an appropriately designed risk-management protocol.

a. _____

b. _____

c. _____

d. _____

e. _____

Multiple-choice Questions

1. What business structure puts a personal trainer at the **GREATEST** risk for losing personal assets in the event of a lawsuit filed by a client for an incident related to personal-training services provided?
   A. C-corporation
   B. Sole proprietorship
   C. Limited liability corporation
   D. Subchapter S-corporation

2. Which business structure combines the limited liability and flow-through taxation of the S-corp with easier creation and operation requirements?
   A. Partnership
   B. C-corporation
   C. Limited liability partnership
   D. Sole proprietorship

3. What is a personal trainer **MOST** likely to give up when switching from working as an independent contractor to working as an employee of a fitness facility?
   A. Social Security taxes being withheld and matched by the facility
   B. Medical benefits covered by the facility
   C. Need for justification from the facility before being fired
   D. Flexibility to set own schedule and pricing

4. Which of the following business practices would be **MOST** likely to put a facility at risk for improperly categorizing personal trainers as independent contractors?
   A. Allowing independent contractors to set their own schedules
   B. Requiring all personal trainers to follow the same assessment and programming procedures
   C. Allowing independent contractors to set their own fees
   D. Requiring all personal trainers to hold their own professional liability insurance

5. What is the **BEST** method for ensuring that all aspects of a client–personal trainer relationship are properly established?
   A. Signed contract
   B. Informed consent
   C. Liability waiver
   D. Verbal agreement

6. In which scenario is the personal trainer **MOST** likely to be found guilty of negligence?
   A. The trainer suffers a low-back injury while spotting a client
   B. The client gets injured on her way into the fitness facility for her training session
   C. The trainer is talking with another club member while the client injures himself due to poor form
   D. The client follows his program but adds two more sets on all exercises and sustains an injury as a result

7. What is the legal term used to describe a situation where a trainer fails to act and a client is injured, but the client is determined to have played a role in his or her own injury?
   A. Contributory negligence
   B. Gross negligence
   C. Complete negligence
   D. Comparative negligence

8. What form is used to have the client acknowledge that he or she has been specifically informed about the risks associated with the activity in which he or she is about to engage?
   A. Liability waiver
   B. Informed consent
   C. Agreement to participate
   D. Exculpatory clause

9. Personal trainers who provide training sessions to individuals and/or groups in clients' homes or outdoor settings should check with their current insurance providers to see if they are covered for training in these settings or if they need to add a(n) _____ policy to their existing professional liability insurance.
   A. General liability insurance
   B. Keyman insurance
   C. Umbrella insurance
   D. Specific insurance rider

10. Which of the following would violate intellectual property laws?
    A. Using music specifically designed for use in fitness facilities during small-group personal training
    B. ACE-certified Professionals using the ACE-certified logo on their business website or clothing
    C. Allowing personal-training clients the option to bring their own music to be played during their training sessions
    D. Using the ACE-certified logo to promote nutritional products, DVDs, or equipment sold by an ACE-certified Professional

Show What You Know

I.   Case Analysis: Analyze the following situation and describe (a) the argument the plaintiff would most likely pursue, (b) the argument the defendant would most likely pursue, (c) the rationale a judge might use to decide the case, and (d) what could have been done to reduce the risk of liability.

Weeble vs. ReallyFit Personal Training Services
Robert Weeble, who is a client of ReallyFit Personal Training Services, dislocated his shoulder during a personal-training session with Doug Bunker at Mr. Weeble's home gym. Doug had asked Mr. Weeble to find something suitable to place under his heels for the squat exercise and Mr. Weeble found two pieces of wood glued together in his garage. Doug examined the wood, placed it on the floor, and said "This will do!" During the squat exercise, the wood came unglued and Mr. Weeble fell down and dislocated his shoulder. _____

_____

_____

_____

_____

_____

_____

_____

_____

_____

_____

_____

Practice What You Know

Perform a risk-management assessment to evaluate the risk of hazards for your clients and your business.

CHAPTER 18

Personal-training Business Fundamentals

Summary Review

A personal trainer should have knowledge of the different business environments that he or she might encounter and their role in overall career development.

The Direct Employee Model

A personal trainer should consider the following factors when making a decision about whether or not to work for an employer:

- Clientele
- Location of facility
- Reputation of the company
- Requirements for employment
- Production expectations of the company
- The various advantages of working in the direct employee model
- The various disadvantages of working in the direct employee model

The Independent Contractor Model

A personal trainer should consider the following factors when making a decision about whether or not to work as an independent contractor:

- How much to charge for services
- Which facility to use
- The type and amount of operational costs that will be incurred
- Which health-screening forms and legal documents to use
- The various advantages of working as an independent contractor
- The various disadvantages of working as an independent contractor

Business Planning

To have a successful career, a personal trainer should take the time to perform an assessment of his or her own financial fitness and use that information to develop a business plan that includes the following components:

- Executive summary
- Business description
- Marketing plan
- Operational plan
- Risk analysis
  ✓ SWOT analysis
- Decision-making criteria

Creating a Brand

A personal trainer should use the business-planning process to develop a brand identity for his or her training service:

- Conducting market research
- Targeting clientele
- Communicating a unique brand identity
- Creating a personal vision statement

A personal trainer should have the ability to promote, develop, and maintain his or her services by applying concepts related to the following business-related topics:

- Communicating the benefits
- Marketing for client retention
- Marketing through general communication

Choosing a Business Structure

When starting a business, a personal trainer should consider the following areas of business ownership:

- How to structure the business
- Whether to work with partners
- Whether to establish a corporate structure

Professional Services for Starting a Business

A personal trainer should consider the services provided by the following professionals when starting a business:

- Attorney
- Accountant
- Web developer/graphic designer
- Insurance broker
- Real estate broker
- Contractors

Financial Plan

To be successful, personal trainers should establish budget and revenue goals for themselves:

- Identify expenses
- Identify revenues
- Set income goals
- Identify specific details for how the business will generate cash flow and produce a profit

Time Management

It is important for personal trainers to develop a schedule that accommodates all of their needs while taking into account the following activities:

- Working with clients
- Client management
- Prospecting for new clients
- Developing marketing or advertising materials
- Other job duties

How to Sell Personal Training

A personal trainer should have an understanding of the following concepts and strategies while selling his or her services:

- Effectively communicating how the knowledge and skills of a personal trainer can meet or exceed the needs of a potential client
- Asking for the sale
- Seven basic rules for selling
- Four basic questions that are required to move from presenting information to closing the sale
- Selling training programs versus selling training sessions

Getting Started

This chapter provides the basics of running a personal-training business, including business planning, marketing, and financial planning. It also explains the advantages and disadvantages of working as an independent contractor or direct employee. After completing this chapter, you will have a better understanding of:

- How to develop a sound business plan
- How to create a brand and communicate the benefits of a business
- Marketing to acquire new clients and retain existing ones
- The professional services needed to run a successful business, including an attorney, accountant, and web developer
- How to sell personal-training services

Reading Assignment

Read Chapter 18 of the *ACE Personal Trainer Manual*, 4th edition, paying special attention to the boldface terms in the chapter. After you have read the chapter, define those terms on a separate piece of paper.

Expand Your Knowledge

I.   Place an (E) beside each item that more likely describes an employee and a (C) beside
     each item that more likely describes an independent contractor.
     a. _____ Receives bonuses when he or she meets certain performance objectives
     b. _____ Works with clients in their own homes
     c. _____ Pays marketing expenses to reach new clients
     d. _____ Has paid vacations
     e. _____ Pays quarterly taxes
     f. _____ Receives a W-2 from the facility owner
     g. _____ Is consulted regarding the layout of the fitness floor
     h. _____ Has to work a minimum number of hours each week
     i. _____ Pays a monthly fee to the fitness facility
     j. _____ Establishes fees based on what the market will pay

II. Describe how the daily flow of members in and out of the club varies between a typical
     suburban facility and a typical urban facility. _____
     _____
     _____
     _____

III. Explain the potential consequences of training "under the table" at a fitness facility.
     _____
     _____
     _____
     _____

IV. Generally speaking, what is the best way to get started as a personal trainer and learn
     about the fitness industry? Provide reasons to support your choice. _____
     _____
     _____
     _____
     _____
     _____

V. List and briefly describe the six components of a business plan.

a. _____
   _____
   _____

b. _____
   _____
   _____

c. _____
   _____
   _____

d. _____
   _____
   _____

e. _____
   _____
   _____

f. _____
   _____
   _____

VI. In which of the six components of the business plan should the following information be included?

a. A short biography for each member of the management team _____
   _____

b. A statement from the board of directors of a local charity thanking the trainer for volunteering to help prepare people to complete a charity 10K race _____
   _____

c. The highlights of why the business plan will be a successful business venture _____
   _____

d. The number of clients who have agreed to follow the trainer to a new location _____
   _____

e. A description of the local fitness market, including potential future competitors ____
   _____

f. The plan for communicating the benefits of the trainer's specific brand of training
   _____

g. The SWOT analysis _____
   _____

h. An explanation of the business structure that will be used _____

_____

i. A list of the costs associated with starting the business, including employee salaries

_____

VII. What are the two basic goals for the personal trainer during the initial session with a new member or prospective client? _____

_____

VIII. Explain how doing each of the following can help a trainer attract new clients.

a. Spending extra time on the fitness floor _____

_____

b. Offering small-group training sessions for three to five participants _____

_____

c. Leading step-training and yoga classes as part of the facility's group fitness schedule

_____

_____

d. Creating an adherence program for current clients _____

_____

IX. List seven factors to consider when contemplating whether to start a personal-training business.

a. _____

b. _____

c. _____

d. _____

e. _____

f. _____

g. _____

ACE Personal Trainer Master the Manual

Multiple-choice Questions

1. What is one potential disadvantage of the direct-employee business model for personal trainers?
   A. The trainer often receives benefits such as medical insurance, paid vacation days, and contributions towards retirement
   B. The employer covers all marketing costs and efforts
   C. The trainer can earn a competitive per-session wage, but generally less than independent contractor per-session wages
   D. The employer pays for equipment purchases and maintenance

2. Which of the following situations would put an independent contractor at risk for prosecution?
   A. Renting training space from a fitness facility
   B. Training in clients' homes using their equipment
   C. Deciding not to train clients at a facility that utilizes practices the trainer feels to be unethical
   D. Training clients for a fee in a facility without notifying or paying the facility owner

3. The mission statement and business model should be detailed in which component of the business plan?
   A. Business description
   B. Operational plan
   C. Executive summary
   D. Marketing plan

4. When conducting a SWOT analysis, where should a personal trainer list the following entry: "the club is unable to meet the needs of the current volume of potential personal-training clientele"?
   A. Strengths
   B. Weaknesses
   C. Opportunities
   D. Threats

5. What is the **BEST** way for a personal trainer to establish relatively immediate emotional connections with clients by defining the quality of personal-training services clients can expect?
   A. Writing a well-detailed business description
   B. Developing a strong brand
   C. Writing a good executive summary
   D. Developing a strong operational plan

6. Which of the following would be the **LEAST** effective method for a personal trainer to attract potential new clients?
   A. Teaching several group exercise classes each week
   B. Offering complimentary monthly talks on timely fitness topics
   C. Posting a trainer profile filled with personal athletic achievements
   D. Leading a free group-training session for a local running event

7. Which of the following would **MOST** likely be seen as a limitation by a client participating in small-group personal training?
   A. Another participant in the group who requires constant individual attention from the trainer
   B. Social support and encouragement received by others in the group
   C. Dissociation from the unpleasant sensations of vigorous exercise due to interaction with others
   D. Personal commitment to adhere to the exercise sessions due to group dynamics

8. In addition to marketing personal-training services to clients, what other skill must a personal trainer develop to become successful at selling training sessions?
   A. Designing good exercise programs
   B. Being able to ask for the sale
   C. Dressing professionally
   D. Maintaining a high level of fitness

9. Which of the following is an example of a question that focuses on the needs of the client?
   A. "What has kept you from achieving your goals in the past?"
   B. "Would you be interested in the camaraderie of small-group personal training sessions?"
   C. "How did you find out about our personal-training services?"
   D. "Would you be interested in the weight-loss training package that we offer?"

10. What is an advantage of selling personal-training programs that have a specific outcome focus such as weight loss or preparation for a specific event?
    A. They increase client motivation because they generally guarantee success
    B. They help weed out clients who are unlikely to commit to a long-term training program
    C. They allow personal trainers to put multiple clients on the same program to save time and effort
    D. They foster program adherence, as clients begin the program with a specific goal in mind

Show What You Know

I. Calculate the number of sessions that a trainer would have to conduct each week if his annual income goal is $60,000, assuming he earns $40 per session and would like to have two weeks of paid vacation each year. _____

_____

_____

_____

_____

_____

_____

II. A beginning trainer has determined that her monthly expenses are approximately $3,000. She has been offered a position at a local health club where she will take home $20 per one-hour training session and $12 per hour spent on the fitness floor. As a condition of her employment, she must spend a minimum of 20 hours each week on the fitness floor helping club members and providing new-member orientation sessions. How many sessions does she need to conduct each day in order to meet her monthly expenses? In this scenario, how many hours will she be working each week? _____

_____

_____

_____

_____

_____

_____

Practice What You Know

I. If you have a business plan, review it to determine where you might make improvements. If you do not have one, use this chapter as a starting point and develop one, even if you are just getting started as a personal trainer.

II. Perform a SWOT analysis and think about how each of your weaknesses can be turned into opportunities.

III. Review the analysis presented as an example on page 635 and perform a similar analysis of the membership of the facility where you work. How does your analysis help you create a vision statement and fine-tune your branding efforts?

APPENDIX A
Certification Information Guide

I. Purpose

The purpose of this information is to provide you with insight into the American Council on Exercise's (ACE) certification process. By understanding how the examination is developed, we believe you can better prepare for the exam. ACE follows the highest standards for professional and occupational certification tests, taking measures to uphold validity, reliability, and fairness for all candidates in our examinations.

II. How is the exam developed?

The ACE certification examinations are developed by ACE and volunteer committees of experts in the field(s) in cooperation with CASTLE Worldwide, Inc., an independent testing agency. The exam development process involves the following steps:

A. Job Analysis

A committee of experts in the fitness field thoroughly analyzes the job requirements and develops an outline of the knowledge and skills necessary to perform the job competently.

B. Validation Study

A research survey is then conducted to determine if the job analysis is valid. This survey is sent to thousands of randomly selected fitness professionals for input and validation. The final outcome is the Exam Content Outline (see Appendix B in the *ACE Personal Trainer Manual*).

C. Item Writing

A national panel of experts develops questions for the exam. Questions are tied specifically to the validated Exam Content Outline, which resulted from the job analysis. All questions are also referenced to an acceptable text or document and further validated for importance, criticalness, and relevance. CASTLE then reviews the questions for the degree to which they adhere to generally accepted testing guidelines.

D. Exam Construction

The questions are then reviewed in detail one more time by the examination committee before being placed on the final exam forms.

E. Cut Score Determination

Once the final exam is constructed, the exam committee rates the difficulty of each question and the passing point is then determined by statistical analysis of the committee ratings. This analysis adjusts for variability in the ratings and gives benefit to the test candidate.

F. Continual Exam Evaluation

Once the exam process is completed, continual evaluation and analysis of each question help to ensure validity. The examination is revised each year, with items being reworked or replaced. Approximately every five years the exam-development process begins again with a new job analysis.

III. How is the exam administered?

An independent testing agency is used to administer all ACE examinations to ensure exam security, integrity, and the elimination of bias. Be assured that all of the policies that ACE follows concerning exam administration are required to maintain these high standards.

IV. Who is eligible to take the exam?

Anyone who is at least 18 years of age and has a valid CPR certification is eligible to take the ACE certification exam. For the ACE Personal Trainer Certification Examination it is assumed that the examinee will be competent in the areas described in the Exam Content Outline found in Appendix B of the *ACE Personal Trainer Manual.* For information concerning fees, registration procedures, and testing dates and sites, please contact ACE at the following address for an Exam Information Brochure.

American Council on Exercise
4851 Paramount Drive
San Diego, CA 92123
(800) 825-3636
www.acefitness.org

APPENDIX B

Answer Key

Chapter 1: Role and Scope of Practice for the Personal Trainer

Expand Your Knowledge

I. (a) Regular physical activity reduces the risk of many adverse health outcomes. (b) Some physical activity is better than none. (c) For most health outcomes, additional benefits occur as the amount of physical activity increases through higher intensity, greater frequency, and/or longer duration. (d) Most health benefits occur with at least 150 minutes a week of moderate-intensity physical activity, such as brisk walking. Additional benefits occur with more physical activity. (e) Both aerobic (endurance) and muscle-strengthening (resistance) physical activity are beneficial. (f) Health benefits occur for children and adolescents, young and middle-aged adults, older adults, and those in every studied racial and ethnic group. (g) The health benefits of physical activity occur for people with disabilities. (h) The benefits of physical activity far outweigh the possibility of adverse outcomes.

II. The *2008 Guidelines* mark the first time the U.S. government has confirmed that fitness is an important part of medicine and that fitness professionals are important members of the allied healthcare continuum.

III. (a) Increasing numbers of baby boomers who want to stay healthy, physically fit, and independent; (b) Reduction in the number of physical-education programs in schools; (c) Growing concerns about childhood obesity; (d) Increasing club memberships among young adults concerned about physical fitness; (e) An aging population seeking relief from arthritis and other ailments through individualized exercise, yoga, and Pilates; (f) A need to replace workers who leave fitness occupations each year

IV. (a) Physicians and nurses; (b) Physical and occupational therapists; (c) Athletic trainers; (d) Registered dietitians

V. (a) Provide safe and effective instruction; (b) Provide equal and fair treatment to all clients; (c) Stay up-to-date on the latest health and fitness research and understand its practical application; (d) Maintain current CPR certification and knowledge of first-aid services; (e) Comply with all applicable business, employment, and intellectual property laws; (f) Maintain the confidentiality of all client information; (g) Refer clients to more qualified health or medical professionals when appropriate; (h) Uphold and enhance public appreciation and trust for the health and fitness industry; (i) Establish and maintain clear professional boundaries

VI. A scope of practice defines the legal range of services that professionals in a given field can provide, the setting in which those services can be provided, and the guidelines or parameters that must be followed.

VII. (a) Not being able to advertise the fact that they hold the ACE certification until it is renewed; (b) Discontinued professional liability insurance; (c) Loss of employment

VIII. (a) A; (b) I; (c) I; (d) I; (e) A

IX. (a) Checking if the course will be at the appropriate level; (b) Seeing if the instructor has the appropriate qualifications to teach the course, (c) Learning if the course is ACE-approved or will have to be petitioned for continuing education credits; (d) Determining if the education provided is within the scope of practice

Multiple-choice Questions

(1) C; (2) B; (3) D; (4) A; (5) D; (6) A; (7) C; (8) B; (9) B; (10) D

Chapter 2: Principles of Adherence and Motivation

Expand Your Knowledge

I. (a) Motivation; (b) 50; (c) Adherence; (d) Activity history

II. (a) P; (b) P; (c) E; (d) A; (e) P; (f) A; (g) P; (h) E; (i) P; (j) E

III. (a) Locus of control is defined as the degree to which people attribute outcomes to internal factors, such as effort and ability, as opposed to external factors, such as luck or the actions of others. A belief in personal control over health outcomes is a consistent predictor of unsupervised exercise activity among healthy adults. (b) Social support from family and friends is an important predictor of physical-activity behavior. It is difficult for an individual to maintain an exercise program if he or she does not have support at home. (c) The drop-out rate in vigorous-intensity exercise programs is almost twice as high as in moderate-intensity activity programs.

IV. (a) Creating mastery; (b) Providing consistent and clear feedback; (c) Including the client in aspects of program design; (d) Creating a workout environment that is aesthetically pleasing

V. The belief in one's own capabilities to successfully engage in a physical-activity program.

VI. (a) Professionalism; (b) Confidentiality; (c) Effective listening; (d) Excitement for the craft; (e) Caring about each client's success

VII. (a) Specific, measurable, attainable, relevant, and time-bound; (b) Setting negative goals puts the focus on the behavior that should be avoided. It is important that the client is thinking about achievement, not avoidance. (c) In every workout; (d) Revisit goals on a regular basis, adjusting them as needed.

Multiple-choice Questions
(1) C; (2) B; (3) D; (4) C; (5) A; (6) A; (7) D; (8) B; (9) B; (10) C

Show What You Know
I. Modify Joe's exercise program to make it less physically challenging by including small breaks or decreasing the intensity of the exercises. Also, emphasize the physical and mental health benefits of Joe's new program.

II. Emphasize short-term benefits of physical activity when the client becomes discouraged about meeting the long-term goals, or when the immediate discomfort of exercise does not seem to be paying off for the client.

Chapter 3: Communication and Teaching Techniques

Expand Your Knowledge
I. (a) Positive experiences are characterized by a sense of caring, respect, clear communication, and professionalism. Clients perceive that their concerns are taken seriously and that the personal trainer is highly qualified, knowledgeable, and helpful. Questions are carefully considered and clearly answered. The environment is usually clean and organized. (b) Negative experiences are marked by rudeness, indifference, ineptitude, neglect, and malpractice. People often report being left waiting for a long time in environments that are dirty, disorganized, or dull. Personal trainers are described as appearing bored, uninterested in the client, uncaring, or distracted. Communications with personal trainers are perceived as unclear, with clients saying they did not understand the information or the reasons for the recommendations. Questions are not encouraged or answered clearly.

II. (a) body language; verbal content; (b) process; product; Process; (c) extrinsic; (d) Cultural competence

III. (a) Voice quality; (b) Eye contact; (c) Facial expression; (d) Hand gestures; (e) Body position

IV.

	Low Sociability		
Low Dominance	Deliberator	Director	High Dominance
	Collaborator	Expressor	
	High Sociability		

V. (a) 3; (b) 4; (c) 1; (d) 2

VI. (a) 5; (b) 2; (c) 3; (d) 1; (e) 4

VII. (a) Listen carefully to understand what clients hope to accomplish with an exercise program. (b) Help them define specific, measurable goals. (c) Suggest additional goals that clients may not have thought of, such as feeling more energetic and less stressed. (d) Break large goals (reachable in six months or more) into small goals (reachable in about eight to 10 weeks) and even weekly goals (such as completing a certain number of exercise sessions). (e) Include many process goals, such as the completion of exercise sessions. In other words, simply completing workouts accomplishes a goal. (f) Record goals and set up a record-keeping system to record workouts and track progress toward goals. (g) Be sure clients understand what types of exercise will help them reach their health and fitness goals. (h) Reevaluate and revise goals and exercise recommendations periodically to prevent discouragement if large goals are not being met.

VIII. Self-monitoring systems help in two ways. First, they increase client self-awareness. A log with nothing recorded for several days testifies to the fact that clients are neglecting their exercise programs. Self-

monitoring acts as a mirror to give clients a more objective view of their behaviors. Second, self-monitoring systems enhance client–trainer communication. Clients come to expect careful surveillance of their records, which they present to the personal trainer at each session. Knowing that someone will be checking on their adherence may prod clients into action.
IX.   b
X.   (a) 1; (b) 3; (c) 2

Multiple-choice Questions
(1) D; (2) A; (3) D; (4) C; (5) A; (6) B; (7) B; (8) B; (9) A; (10) C

Chapter 4: Basics of Behavior Change and Health Psychology

Expand Your Knowledge
I.   (a) 4; (b) 5; (c) 1; (d) 2; (e) 3
II.   (a) Maintenance is the stage of successful, sustained lifestyle modification, while relapse is the opposite of maintenance and generally refers to baseline behavior. (b) Antecedents are stimuli that precede a behavior and are sometimes referred to as cues or triggers, while consequences are stimuli that follow a behavior and may be either positive or negative. (c) During precontemplation, the individual is not intending to change soon and perceives more cons related to physical activity than pros. Individuals who have decided to initiate an effort to change are in the preparation stage. (d) Shaping is the process of using reinforcements to gradually achieve a target behavior, while observational learning consists of seeing others serve as examples and prompts to behavior change. (e) Extinction occurs when a positive stimulus that once followed a behavior is removed, while punishment consists of an aversive stimulus following an undesirable behavior.
III.   The health belief model suggests that individuals adopt (or do not adopt) health behaviors based largely upon their appraisal of their susceptibility to an illness, combined with their perception of the probable severity of the consequences of having the illness.
IV.   (a) individual; (b) Cues to action; (c) self-efficacy; (d) processes of change; (e) Operant conditioning
V.   (a) Past performance experience; (b) Vicarious experience; (c) Verbal persuasion; (d) Physiological state appraisals; (e) Emotion state and mood appraisals; (f) Imaginal experiences
VI.   (a) 4; (b) 5; (c) 1; (d) 3; (e) 2
VII.   (a) PC, C; (b) A, M; (c) PC, C, P, A, M; (d) P; (e) C
VIII.   (a) Stimulus control refers to making adjustments to the environment to increase the likelihood of healthy behaviors. Examples include choosing a gym that is in the direct route between home and work; keeping a gym bag in the car that contains all the required items for a workout; having workout clothes, socks, and shoes laid out for early morning workouts; writing down workout times as part of a weekly schedule, and surrounding oneself with other people who have similar health and fitness goals. (b) These effective behavior-change techniques can be used together or on their own to help people adhere to their programs. A written agreement outlines the expectations of the client and trainer and decreases ambiguity and clarifies the roles of all people involved. A behavioral contract might include an outline of a reward system to increase adherence. (c) Cognitive behavioral techniques target how people think and feel about being physically active. Examples include setting SMART goals, providing proper feedback, decision making, and self-monitoring.

Multiple-choice Questions
(1) A; (2) B; (3) C; (4) D; (5) C; (6) B; (7) A; (8) B; (9) C; (10) D

Chapter 5: Introduction to the ACE Integrated Fitness Training Model

Expand Your Knowledge
I.   (a) Postural (kinetic chain) stability; (b) Kinetic chain mobility; (c) Movement efficiency; (d) Core conditioning; (e) Balance; (f) Cardiorespiratory (aerobic) fitness; (g) Muscular endurance; (h) Muscular strength; (i) Flexibility; (j) Metabolic marker (ventilatory thresholds); (k) Agility, coordination, and reactivity; (l) Speed and power
II.   (a) 150 minutes; 75 minutes; (b) improved health; (c) rapport; (d) posture
III.   (a) To ensure the safety of the client; (b) To provide an opportunity for the personal trainer to establish trust and create an open source of communication
IV.   (a) Functional movement and resistance training; (b) Cardiorespiratory training

V.

Table 5-3				
ACE Integrated Fitness Training Model—Training Components and Phases				
Training Component	**Phase 1**	**Phase 2**	**Phase 3**	**Phase 4**
Functional Movement & Resistance Training	Stability and Mobility Training	Movement Training	Load Training	Performance Training
Cardiorespiratory Training	Aerobic-base Training	Aerobic-efficiency Training	Anaerobic-endurance Training	Anaerobic-power Training

VI. (a) Phase 1: Improving health by correcting imbalances through training to improve joint stability and mobility prior to training movement patterns and building an aerobic base to improve parameters of cardiorespiratory health; (b) Phase 2: Progressing clients toward improved fitness by introducing aerobic intervals to improve aerobic efficiency and training movement patterns prior to loading the movements; (c) Phase 3: Progressing to higher levels of fitness through load training and the development of anaerobic endurance; (d) Phase 4: Improving performance through training for power, speed, agility, reactivity, and anaerobic power.

VII. A complete battery of assessments can be detrimental by reinforcing the client's negative self-image and beliefs that he or she is hopelessly out of shape or obese.

VIII. (a) Changes in hormone and neurotransmitter levels (e.g., endorphins, serotonin, and norepinephrine); (b) Increased self-efficacy with task and possible short-term goal accomplishment; (c) Improved performance due to the positive neuromuscular adaptations to exercise that follow the initial delayed onset muscle soreness and accompanying decreases in strength

IX. (a) 2, 5, 7; (b) 1, 9, 11; (c) 3, 6, 10; (d) 4, 8, 12

X. (a) 3, 4, 5; (b) 1, 6, 9; (c) 7, 8, 10; (d) 2, 11, 12

Multiple-choice Questions

(1) C; (2) B; (3) D; (4) C; (5) A; (6) C; (7) A; (8) B; (9) D; (10) C

Chapter 6: Building Rapport and the Initial Investigation Stage

Expand Your Knowledge

I. (a) Empathy: The ability to experience another person's world as if it were one's own; (b) Warmth: An unconditional positive regard, or respect, for another person regardless of his or her individuality or uniqueness. This quality will convey a climate that communicates safety and acceptance to the client. (c) Genuineness: Authenticity, or the ability to be honest and open

II. Rapport is ongoing, unlike the other three stages, which have somewhat clearly defined timelines.

III. (a) Rapport: Involves the personal interaction a trainer establishes and maintains with a client, as well as the ability to communicate effectively with clients. (b) Investigation: Involves the collection of all relevant information to identify the comprehensive needs of clients. (c) Planning: Involves collaborative goal setting with the client after the investigation is complete to design an effective and comprehensive program. (d) Action: Involves the successful implementation of all programming components and providing the appropriate instruction, feedback, and progression as needed.

IV. To build a foundation for a personal relationship with the individual.

V. (a) Create a nurturing, yet professional environment by meeting in a quiet, comfortable area. (b) Avoid high-traffic areas and member distractions, and do not attempt to establish rapport with a simple facility tour or orientation. (c) Do not sit behind a desk, but rather sit facing the client to create a level of comfort.

VI.   (a) A person is not really listening and is tuned out. (b) A person listens only to key words. (c) A person gives the impression of listening by using minimal noncommittal agreements. (d) A person shows empathy and listens as if he or she is in the speaker's shoes.

VII.   (a) Motivational interviewing; (b) stages-of-change; (c) PAR-Q; (d) one; (e) high-density lipoprotein cholesterol

VIII.   (a) Identifying the presence or absence of known cardiovascular, pulmonary, and/or metabolic disease, or signs or symptoms suggestive of cardiovascular, pulmonary, and/or metabolic disease; (b) Identifying individuals with medical contraindications (health conditions and risk factors) who should be excluded from exercise or physical activity until those conditions have been corrected or are under control; (c) Detecting at-risk individuals who should first undergo medical evaluation and clinical exercise testing before initiating an exercise program; (d) Identifying those individuals with medical conditions who should participate in medically supervised programs

IX.   (a) Identifying coronary artery disease (CAD) risk factors; (b) Performing a risk stratification based on CAD risk factors; (c) Determining the need for a medical exam/clearance and medical supervision

X.   (a) X; (d) X; (e) X; (f) X

XI.   (a) 2, 4, 7; (b) 1, 8; (c) 3, 10; (d) 6, 9; (e) 5, 12; (f) 11

XII.   (a) stroke; (b) Dyspnea; (c) overuse injury; (d) cross-training; (e) diabetes

XIII.   (a) Reduces the force of contraction; (b) Opens or dilates them to allow more room for the blood; (c) Reduces the sympathetic nerve outflow; (d) Depletes body water and decreases blood volume

XIV.   (a) 1; (b) 3; (c) 2; (d) 5; (e) 4

XV.   (a) Onset of angina pectoris or angina-like symptoms that center around the chest; (b) Significant drop (>10 mmHg) in systolic blood pressure despite an increase in exercise intensity; (c) Excessive rise in blood pressure: SBP >250 mmHg or DBP >115 mmHg; (d) Fatigue, shortness of breath, difficult or labored breathing, or wheezing (does not include heavy breathing due to intense exercise); (e) Signs of poor perfusion: lightheadedness, pallor, cyanosis, nausea, or cold and clammy skin; (f) Increased nervous system symptoms (e.g., ataxia, dizziness, confusion, syncope); (g) Leg cramping

or claudication; (h) Physical or verbal manifestations of severe fatigue

XVI.   (a) Goals of the assessment; (b) Physical limitations of the participant; (c) Testing environment; (d) Availability of equipment; (e) Age of the participant

Multiple-choice Questions

(1) B; (2) D; (3) C; (4) B; (5) A; (6) A; (7) B; (8) C; (9) D; (10) A

Chapter 7: Functional Assessments: Posture, Movement, Core, Balance, and Flexibility

Expand Your Knowledge

I.   Movement operates from a static base or alignment of the body segments, which is commonly referred to as posture. Since movement originates from this base, a postural assessment should be conducted to evaluate body-segment alignment in addition to movement screens that evaluate how posture, both good and bad, impacts the ability to move.

II.   That state of musculoskeletal alignment and balance that allows muscles, joints, and nerves to function efficiently

III.   (a) Repetitive movements; awkward positions and movements; side dominance; lack of joint stability; lack of joint mobility; imbalanced strength-training programs; (b) Congenital conditions; some pathologies; structural deviations; certain types of trauma

IV.   Since individuals may consciously or subconsciously attempt to correct posture when they are aware they are being observed, distractions such as casual conversation may relax the client and lead to a more normal, relaxed position.

V.   (a) This client may stand in a more pronated position. (b) This client may stand in a more supinated position.

VI.   A pronated ankle position typically forces internal rotation of the tibia and slightly less internal rotation of the femur. Ankle pronation also forces rotation at the knee and places additional stresses on some knee ligaments and the integrity of the joint itself. Additionally, as pronation tends to move the calcaneus into eversion, this may actually lift the outside of the heel slightly off the ground (moving the ankle into plantarflexion). In turn, this may tighten the calf muscles and limit dorsiflexion. Ankle pronation may also lead to an anterior pelvic tilt, and therefore lumbar lordosis.

VII. Hip tilting (anterior)

VIII. (a) Hip flexors, erector spinae; (b) Rectus abdominis, hamstrings; (c) Cervical spine extensors, upper trapezius, levator scapulae

IX. (a) Bending/raising and lifting/lowering movements (e.g., squatting); (b) Single-leg movements; (c) Pushing movements (in vertical/horizontal planes) and resultant movement; (d) Pulling movements (in vertical/horizontal planes) and resultant movement; (e) Rotational movements

X. Refer the client to his or her physician and do not have the client perform additional assessments for that part of the body.

XI. (a) Gluteus medius and maximus; (b) Core, rectus abdominis, gluteal group, hamstrings; (c) Medial gastrocnemius, gracilis, sartorius, tibialis group

XII. To examine simultaneous mobility of one limb and stability of the contralateral limb while maintaining both hip and torso stabilization under a balance challenge of standing on one leg

XIII. (b) Trainers should not cue the client to use good technique, as it is important to observe the client's natural movement.

XIV. A lack of core stability

XV. Rectus femoris

XVI. (a) Shoulder extension and flexion; (b) Internal and external rotation of the humerus at the shoulder; (c) Scapular abduction and adduction

XVII. (a) The client loses postural control and balance; (b) The client's feet move on the floor; (c) The client's eyes open; (d) The client's arms move from the folded position; (e) The client exceeds 60 seconds with good postural control

XVIII. The ability to draw the abdominal wall inward via coordinated action of the transverse abdominis and related core muscles without activation of the rectus abdominis

Multiple-choice Questions

(1) C; (2) A; (3) C; (4) D; (5) B; (6) D; (7) C; (8) B; (9) A; (10) B

Show What You Know

I. You should test Eileen's shoulder position relative to her thoracic spine. One likely cause of her pain is a torso lean that shifts the alignment of the sternum (anterior) and spine (posterior), thereby creating tightness in the flexed side of the trunk. This tightness would explain why the shoulders are not level and may create uneven spacing between the arms and the torso.

Chapter 8: Physiological Assessments

Expand Your Knowledge

I. (a) Cardiorespiratory fitness; (b) Body composition; (c) Muscular endurance; (d) Muscular strength; (e) Flexibility

II. (a) Anaerobic power; (b) Anaerobic capacity; (c) Speed; (d) Agility; (e) Reactivity; (f) Coordination

III. (a) Onset of angina, chest pain, or angina-like symptoms; (b) Significant drop (>10 mmHg) in systolic blood pressure (SBP) despite an increase in exercise intensity; (c) Excessive rise in blood pressure (BP): SBP >250 mmHg or diastolic blood pressure (DBP) >115 mmHg; (d) Excess fatigue, shortness of breath, or wheezing (does not include heavy breathing due to intense exercise); (e) Signs of poor perfusion: lightheadedness, pallor (pale skin), cyanosis (bluish coloration, especially around the mouth), nausea, or cold and clammy skin; (f) Increased nervous system symptoms (e.g., ataxia, dizziness, confusion, syncope); (g) Leg cramping or claudication; (h) Subject requests to stop; (i) Physical or verbal manifestations of severe fatigue; (j) Failure of testing equipment

IV. (a) Body composition refers to the proportion of lean tissue to body-fat tissue, while body mass index only takes into account a person's height and weight. (b) Overweight is defined as an upward deviation in body weight based on the subject's height, while overfat is a more accurate depiction of body composition that indicates an excess amount of body fat. (c) MRI uses a magnetic field to assess how much fat a person has and where it is deposited, while NIR uses a fiber optic probe connected to a digital analyzer that indirectly measures tissue composition. (d) Android describes apple-shaped individuals who carry excess fat in the abdominal area, while gynoid describes pear-shaped individuals who carry excess fat in the hips, buttocks, and thighs.

V. No strict guidelines exist, but every one to two months is appropriate.

VI. (a) ≥95; (b) ≥86

VII. The ability to perform large muscle movement over a sustained period; related to the capacity of the heart-lung system to deliver oxygen for sustained energy production

VIII. (a) Heart rate; (b) Blood pressure; (c) Ratings of perceived exertion; (d) Signs and symptoms

IX.   (a) The Balke & Ware treadmill test; (b) Beta blockers would make the test invalid, as they blunt heart-rate response; (c) The client may be at risk for hypoglycemia, and the test should be postponed until after he has eaten and his blood glucose level has been rechecked.

X.   (a) Obese individuals who are not comfortable on the standard seats or are physically unable to pedal at the appropriate cadence; (b) Individuals with orthopedic problems that limit knee range of motion to less than 110 degrees; (c) Individuals with neuromuscular problems who cannot maintain a cadence of 50 rotations per minute

XI.   (a) It is easier to manually measure exercise heart rate and blood pressure because the arms are relatively stationary as compared to treadmill testing. (b) Cycle ergometer testing is better suited for individuals with balance problems or unfamiliarity with the treadmill.

XII.   (a) VT1; (b) VT2; (c) VT1; (d) VT1; (e) VT2; (f) VT2

XIII.   The heart rate at VT1 can be used as a target heart rate when determining exercise intensity. Those interested in sports conditioning and/or competition would benefit from training at higher intensities, but those interested in health and general fitness are well-served to stay at or slightly below this exercise intensity.

XIV.   The lactate threshold and corresponding VT2 are commonly related to performance. For example, if two athletes with the same $\dot{V}O_2$max are competing, the athlete with the higher lactate threshold will likely outperform the other athlete. Lactate threshold is improved by endurance training and high-intensity training (up to 105% of $\dot{V}O_2$max). At these intense training levels, the body can respond and adapt to the increased workloads, thereby "clearing" the blood lactate at a more efficient rate.

XV.   (a) Individuals who are extremely overweight; (b) Individuals with balance problems; (c) Individuals with orthopedic problems; (d) Individuals who are extremely deconditioned; (e) Individuals who are short in stature

XVI.   Muscular-endurance testing assesses the ability of a specific muscle group, or groups, to perform repeated or sustained contractions to sufficiently invoke muscular fatigue.

XVII.   The test should be immediately terminated and the client should be referred to his or her personal physician. Muscular-endurance testing should not be conducted until this client has consulted with a physician.

XVIII. To evaluate balanced core strength and

stability, it is important to assess all sides of the torso. The true value of McGill's tests is in the assessment of the interrelationships among the results of the three torso tests. Poor endurance capacity of the torso muscles or an imbalance between these three muscle groups is believed to contribute to low-back dysfunction and core instability.

XIX.   (a) 140/130 = 1.1; (b) 93/95 = 0.98; (c) 95/130 = 0.73; (d) While the RSB:LSB ratio and the LSB:extension ratio fall within McGill's recommendations, the flexion:extension ratio of 1.1 is outside of those recommendations. This imbalance will need to be addressed during the early stages of the training program.

XX.   1-RM testing, which should only be conducted with advanced exercisers in stages 3 or 4 of the ACE IFT model, measures the greatest amount of weight that a client can lift one time. Submaximal strength testing, which is more suitable for most clients, yields results that can be used to estimate the client's 1 RM.

XXI.   Power is the rate at which mechanical work is performed and it correlates to the immediate energy available through the anaerobic energy system, specifically the phosphagen energy system.

XXII.   These types of tests are most appropriate for clients interested in training at phase 4 of the ACE IFT Model or who are athletic or highly fit.

Multiple-choice Questions
(1) D; (2) B; (3) C; (4) C; (5) B; (6) A; (7) A; (8) B; (9) D; (10) A

Show What You Know
I.   (a) Fat weight = Current body weight x Body-fat percentage (BF%) = 230 lb x 33% = 76 lb of fat; (b) Lean body weight = Total weight − Fat weight = 230 lb − 76 lb = 154 lb of lean tissue; (c) Goal weight = Current lean body weight/(100% − Goal BF%) = 154 lb/0.71 = 217 lb

Chapter 9: Functional Programming for Stability-Mobility and Movement

Expand Your Knowledge
I.   (a) Joint stability is the ability to maintain or control joint movement or position, while joint mobility is the range of uninhibited movement around a joint or body segment. (b) Proximal means nearest to the midline of the body or point of origin of a muscle,

while distal means farthest from the midline of the body or point of origin of a muscle. (c) The length-tension relationship is the relationship between the contractile proteins of a sarcomere and their force-generating capacity, while force-couple relationships are seen when multiple muscles function as an integrated group by providing opposing, directional, or contralateral pulls at joints. (d) Reciprocal inhibition is defined as the reflex inhibition of the motor neurons of antagonists when the agonists are contracted, while synergistic dominance is a condition in which the synergists carry out the primary function of a weakened or inhibited prime mover. (e) Hollowing involves activation of the transverse abdominis that draws the abdomen in toward the spine, while bracing involved the co-contraction of the core and abdominal muscles to create a more rigid and wider base of support for spinal stabilization. (f) Static balance is the ability to maintain the body's center of mass within its base of support, while dynamic balance is the ability to move the body's center of mass outside of its base of support while maintaining postural control and establishing a new base of support.

II.

Glenohumeral = Mobility
Scapulothoracic = Stability
Thoracic spine = Mobility
Lumbar spine = Stability
Hip = Mobility
Knee = Stability
Ankle = Mobility
Foot = Stability

III. (a) Muscle immobilization; (b) Passive shortening; (c) Trauma; (d) Aging

IV. Because the hamstrings are not designed for this function and may suffer from overuse or overload, this scenario increases the likelihood for tightness or injury in the hamstrings. In addition, because the hamstrings do not offer the same degree of movement control of the femoral head during hip extension as the gluteus maximus does, this scenario also increases the likelihood for dysfunctional movement and injury to the hip over time.

V. To reestablish appropriate levels of stability and mobility in the body. This process begins by targeting the lumbar spine, which encompasses the body's center of mass, and the core.

VI. (a) Type I (slow-twitch) muscle fibers enhance a stabilizer muscle's capacity for endurance, which allows the muscle to efficiently stabilize the joint for prolonged periods without undue fatigue. (b) Type II (fast-twitch) muscle fibers are better suited for generating the larger forces necessary to produce joint movements.

VII. (a) Lumbar spine; (b) Proximal mobility; (c) Scapulothoracic spine; Glenohumeral joint; (d) Distal extremities; (e) Static balance

VIII. Lumbo-pelvic region, hips, abdomen, and lower back

IX. (a) While they do offer some segmental stabilization of each individual vertebra, especially at end ranges of motion, these small muscles are rich in sensory nerve endings and provide continuous feedback to the brain regarding loading and position of the spine. (b) The middle layer consists of muscles and fasciae that encircle the lower regions of the spine. Envision a box spanning the vertebrae from the diaphragm to the sacroiliac joint and pelvic floor, with muscles enclosing the back, front, and sides. This box allows the spinal and sacroiliac joints to stiffen in anticipation of loading and movement, and provides a solid, stable working foundation from which the body can operate. (c) The outermost layer consists of larger, more powerful muscles that span many vertebrae and are primarily responsible for generating gross movement and forces within the trunk.

X. (a) Emphasizes core-activation exercises and isolated stabilization under minimal spine loading; (b) Emphasizes sectional and whole-body (integrated) stabilization under a fixed base of support; (c) Emphasizes whole-body (integrated) stabilization under a dynamic base of support

XI. Only after the individual effectively demonstrates the ability to stabilize the more proximal regions of the body

XII. (a) Narrow the base of support; (b) Raise the center of mass; (c) Shift the line of gravity; (d) Sensory alteration; (e) Sensory removal; (f) Reduce the points of contact; (g) Add unstable surfaces

Multiple-choice Questions

(1) A; (2) B; (3) C; (4) D; (5) A; (6) C; (7) B; (8) D; (9) A; (10) D

ACE Personal Trainer Master the Manual

Show What You Know

I.   (a) Introduction of "drawing-in"; Instruction of supine drawing-in exercises during the first 20 minutes of each session with instructions to perform exercises once or twice each day outside of the training sessions; Progress volume from 1 set x 10 repetitions to 3 sets x 10 repetitions over the week; (b) Instruction of new quadruped exercises during the first 15 minutes of each session with instructions to perform exercises once or twice each day outside of the training sessions; Progress volume from 2 sets x 10 repetitions to 4 sets x 10 repetitions over the week; (c) Instruction and participation in seated stability ball exercises during the first 15–20 minutes of each session with demonstrations on how to progress the balance challenge; Progress the duration of each exercise from 2 repetitions x 5–10 seconds to 3 repetitions x 10–15 seconds

Chapter 10: Resistance Training: Programming and Progressions

Expand Your Knowledge

I.   (a) 5 pounds (2.3 kg); (b) When less energy is used for daily metabolic function, calories that were previously used by muscle tissue (that has atrophied) are stored as fat. (c) Resistance training can increase gastrointestinal transit speed, which may reduce the risk of colon cancer.

II. Increased muscle size and increased muscular strength

III. (a) Myofibrillar hypertrophy is an increase in the number of myofibrils within the muscle fiber; this results in greater muscle contraction force. (b) Sarcoplasmic hypertrophy is an increase in the muscle cell sarcoplasm that surrounds the myofibrils; this does not result in greater muscle contraction force. (c) Transient hypertrophy is caused by fluid accumulation in the spaces between cells and quickly diminishes after exercise; this does not result in greater muscle contraction force.

IV. (a) Individuals who have higher levels of testosterone typically have enhanced potential for muscle development. (b) Due to larger body size, higher lean weight percentage, and more anabolic hormones (testosterone), men typically have greater muscle mass and overall muscular strength than women. However, when compared on a pound-for-pound basis of lean (muscle) weight, male and female subjects show an almost identical capacity for muscle force production. (c) It appears that people of all ages respond favorably to progressive resistance exercise and gain muscle at approximately the same rate during the initial training period. However, the potential for total-body muscle mass diminishes during the older-adult years. (d) Although limb length does not influence muscle hypertrophy, it definitely affects strength performance. Other things being equal, shorter limbs provide leverage advantages over longer limbs.

V.   Muscular power

VI.

Table 10-1	
Health- and Skill-related Parameters	
Health-related Parameters	Skill-related Parameters
Aerobic capacity	Power
Muscular endurance	Speed
Muscular strength	Balance
Flexibility	Agility
Body composition	Coordination
	Reactivity

VII. (b) X

VIII. (a) To allow for adaptation and accommodation to the training stress; (b) To allow the client to feel successful after accomplishing the goal of performing a specific volume of training

IX. (a) the training effort; (b) two to three; three to four; (c) creatine phosphate; (d) 30–90 seconds; 2–5 minutes

X.   Progressing intensity too quickly could lead to muscle soreness or injury, providing reasons for a client to quit the exercise program.

XI. In the double-progressive strength-training protocol, the first progression is adding repetitions and the second progression is adding resistance in 5% increments. For example, if a client can perform eight repetitions on the incline bench press machine with 180 pounds, he remains at that resistance until he can perform 12 repetitions with good form. At that point, he increases the weightload by approximately 5%.

XII. (a) Specific exercise demands made on the body produce specific responses by the body. (b) A physiological system subjected to above-normal stress will respond by increasing in strength or function accordingly. (c) Any improvement in physical fitness due to physical activity is entirely reversible with the discontinuation of the training program. (d) After a certain level of performance has been achieved, there will be a decline in the effectiveness of training at furthering a person's performance level.

XIII. Linear periodization provides a consistent training protocol *within* each microcycle and changes the training variables *after* each microcycle. Undulating periodization provides different training protocols *during* the microcycles in addition to changing the training variables *after* each microcycle.

XIV. The major disadvantage is the use of lower weightloads due to the cumulative effects of fatigue from nearly continuous resistance training. The advantages include shorter training sessions and moderate aerobic conditioning from sustaining relatively high heart rates throughout the exercise session.

XV. (a) S; (b) E; (c) E; (d) H; (e) S; (f) H

XVI. (a) Two or more sequentially performed exercises that target opposing muscle groups are completed; (b) Two or more sequentially performed exercises that target the same muscle group are completed; (c) The exerciser trains to muscle fatigue, then immediately reduces the intensity by 10 to 20% and performs as many additional repetitions as possible to attain a deeper level of muscle fatigue. (d) The exerciser trains to muscle fatigue, then receives manual assistance from a trainer on the lifting phase for three to five post-fatigue repetitions.

XVII. (a) A foundation of strength and joint integrity; (b) Adequate static and dynamic balance; (c) Effective core function; (d) Anaerobic efficiency; (e) Athleticism; (f) No contraindications to load-bearing, dynamic movements; (g) No medical concerns that affect balance and motor skills

XVIII. (a) The feet are the points of contact for lower-body drills. Single-leg drills impart more stress on the body than double-leg drills. (b) Faster movements increase intensity more than slower movements. (c) The higher the body's center of gravity, the greater the forces of impact upon landing. (d) The greater the client's weight, the more intense the drill. Additional external weight can be added to increase the drill's intensity. (e) Increasing the complexity, such as adding more body segments or increasing the balance challenge, increases the intensity of the drill.

XIX. (a) 3; (b) 2; (c) 6; (d) 5; (e) 1; (f) 4

XX. (a) Increasing the speed of movement; (b) Increasing the complexity of the tasks; (c) Increasing the direction of movement; (c) Introducing resistance

XXI. (a) 3; (b) 6; (c) 1; (d) 5; (e) 2; (f) 7; (g) 4

XXII. (a) 1; (b) 3; (c) 4; (d) 2; (e) 6; (f) 5

Multiple-choice Questions

(1) D; (2) B; (3) B; (4) D; (5) C; (6) A; (7) C; (8) A; (9) B; (10) D

Show What You Know

I. (a) Manny: 3 x 12 x 180 = 6480 pounds; Andre: 4 x 8 x 210 = 6720 pounds; Matt: 3 x 4 x 255 = 3060 pounds; (b) Andre, as there is a correlation between the total amount of weight lifted and the total number of calories burned

Chapter 11: Cardiorespiratory Training: Programming and Progressions

Expand Your Knowledge

I. (a) type I muscle fibers (or slow-twitch muscle fibers); mitochondria; (b) type II muscle fibers (or fast-twitch muscle fibers); enzymes; (c) hypertrophy; cardiac output; (d) strength; fatigue resistance; (e) $\dot{V}O_2$max; ventilatory threshold

II. With the first exercise bout

III. A "second wind" is reached when the client reaches a steady state after beginning a workout or increasing exercise intensity. The time needed to reach this level varies according to several factors, including fitness level (more fit individuals reach steady state faster) and exercise intensity (when working at higher intensities, people require longer periods to achieve steady state).

IV. (c) X

V. (a) Perform 150 minutes per week of moderate-intensity aerobic physical activity, or 75 minutes per week of vigorous-intensity aerobic physical activity, or a combination of both. (b) Additional health benefits are obtained from performing greater amounts of activity than those quantities. (c) Perform aerobic bouts that last at least 10 minutes, preferably spread throughout the week. (d) Participate in muscle-strengthening activities involving all major muscle groups at least two days per week.

VI. (a) Perform at least 60 minutes of moderate-to-vigorous physical activity every day. (b) Include vigorous-intensity activity a minimum of three days per week. (c) Participate in muscle-strengthening and bone-strengthening activity a minimum of three days per week.

VII. Frequency, intensity, time (duration)

VIII. (a) 5, 8, 12, 14; (b) 4, 7; (c) 1, 13, 16; (d) 10,

15; (e) 3; (f) 6; (g) 11, 17; (h) 2, 9

IX.   (a) Perform 50 to 60 minutes of moderate-intensity exercise or activity each day, five to seven days a week, for a total of 300 minutes; (b) Perform a total of 150 minutes of vigorous exercise or activity per week, performed over a minimum of three days; (c) A combination of both

X.   Duration

XI.   Immersion in water causes the blood to be redistributed to the central circulation, away from the limbs. In people with compromised circulatory function, this can lead to complications (e.g., breathlessness, heart failure)

XII. (a) Aerobic-base training; (b) Aerobic-efficiency training; (c) Anaerobic-endurance training; (d) Anaerobic-power training

XIII. (a) Phase 2; (b) Phase 3

XIV. (a) Creating positive exercise experiences that help sedentary clients become regular exercisers; (b) Once they can sustain steady-state cardiorespiratory exercise for 20 to 30 minutes in zone 1 and are comfortable with assessments; (c) Increasing the duration of exercise and introducing intervals to improve aerobic efficiency, fitness, and health; (d) If a client has event-specific goals or is a fitness enthusiast looking for increased challenges and fitness gains; *Note:* Many clients will stay in phase 2 for many years. (e) Helping clients who have endurance performance goals and/or are performing seven or more hours of cardiorespiratory exercise per week; (f) Only clients who have very specific goals for increasing speed for shorts bursts at near-maximal efforts during endurance or athletic competitions will move on to phase 4

XV.   Because all exercise falls in zone 1 (i.e., sub-VT1), the trainer can use the client's ability to talk comfortably as the upper exercise-intensity limit.

XVI. Phase 2

XVII. The client will be able to exercise at a lower heart rate when at the same level of intensity, and the client will be able to exercise at higher intensities when at the VT1 heart rate.

XVIII. This intensity has been called a "black hole" because exercise is hard enough in this zone to make a person fatigued, but not hard enough to induce optimal training adaptations.

XIX. (a) Avoiding cardiovascular risk; (b) Avoiding orthopedic risk; (c) The need to preserve muscle tissue; (d) The rate at which older individuals adapt to training

Multiple-choice Questions

(1) A; (2) A; (3) C; (4) B; (5) C; (6) D; (7) B; (8) A; (9) D; (10) B

Show What You Know

I.   For most exercisers, it probably does no harm to do some brief stretching at the *end* of the warm-up, but because very high-intensity elements are to be included in this client's workouts, stretching may actually inhibit the ability to achieve full intensity. This is attributed to the fact that stretching improves muscle elasticity (decreasing tissue viscosity), which lowers the force-generating capacity of the contractile proteins of the muscle. Moreover, the practice of stretching *before* performing any warm-up is not justified and may potentially be harmful. The warm-up may be subdivided into a more general cardiovascular warm-up followed by a more exercise- or event-specific dynamic warm-up (if unique muscular elements are to be performed during the training session).

II.   (a) Even among aerobic exercises, the transfer of benefits from one type of exercise to another is far from 100%. Research demonstrates that activities that use similar muscles (including Dave's choice of cycling in place of running) have about 50% of the value of performing specific training (e.g., running) on a minute-by-minute basis. Muscularly non-similar training (such as Dave's choice of swimming) has only 25% of the value of performing specific training on a minute-by-minute basis. (b) The principle of specificity may provide one explanation for the lack of improvement. The stop-and-go exercise performed during a basketball game, especially in a recreational game that may involve a lot of downtime and may even be half-court, is very different from the constant running performed on a treadmill. In addition, in game-type activities, the cardiorespiratory benefit is proportional to the amount and intensity of ambulatory activity involved. Perhaps Kevin wasn't working as hard during those games as he thought

Chapter 12: The ACE Integrated Fitness Training™ Model in Practice

Multiple-choice Questions

(1) B; (2) C; (3) A; (4) B; (5) D; (6) A; (7) B; (8) C; (9) B; (10) D

Chapter 13: Mind-body Exercise

Expand Your Knowledge

I.   (a) less intense; cognitive; (b) inward mental

focus; (c) yoga; tai chi; (d) tai chi; (e) breath; (f) cardiovascular; pulmonary
II.   (a) Improved muscular strength; (b) Improved flexibility; (c) Improved balance; (d) Improved coordination; (e) Increased mental development; (f) Increased self-efficacy
III.   (a) Moral principles; (b) Observances; (c) Posture; (d) Breath control; (e) Withdrawal of the senses; (f) Concentration; (g) Meditation; (h) Pure contemplation
IV.   (a) 2; (b) 12; (c) 5; (d) 1; (e) 3; (f) 9; (g) 13; (h) 6; (i) 7; (j) 4; (k) 11; (l) 8; (m) 10
V.   (a) Increased muscular strength and flexibility; (b) Increased balance control; (c) Reduced knee arthritis symptoms; (d) Improved posture; (e) Decreased falls in seniors; (f) Decreased low-back pain
VI.   This component refers to the perceptive movement and flow of one's intrinsic energy, vital life force, chi, prana, or other positive energy commonly described in many classical mind-body exercise traditions.
VII.   (a) Diaphragmatic; (b) Nasal; (c) Deep; (d) Smooth; (e) Even; (f) Quiet; (g) Free of pauses
VIII.   (a) Clients should only use forms of mind-body exercise where the degree of difficulty and intensity of effort begins with very low physical effort (e.g., 2–3 METs) and can be graduated slowly. (b) Only those with chronic disease states where the disease course is stable (i.e., no unstable symptoms) should consider mind-body exercise.
IX.   (a) 3; (b) 4; (c) 1, 12; (d) 2, 11; (e) 5; (f) 8; (g) 6; (h) 7; (i) 9; (j) 10

Multiple-choice Questions

(1) A; (2); C; (3) C; (4) A; (5) A; (6) D; (7) B; (8) D; (9) B; (10) A

Show What You Know

I.   Before and during a resistance-training session, he can use two mind-body techniques that are the focuses of nearly all stress-reduction programs: sustained attention to the present and internal awareness. The client should prioritize his mental focus on the kinesthesis of each muscle contraction as well as the breath. This process is in contrast to thoughts generated by the actual physical load or effort, where there is some level of negative appraisal assigned to the difficulty of each exercise repetition. Meditation and yogic-breathing exercises can be integrated with existing warm-up and cool-down exercises. For example, he can begin the warm-up session with a three- to five-minute quiet contemplation or meditation session before progressing to low-level aerobic or flexibility exercise. He can also incorporate

a mind-body component in the aerobic phase of an exercise session. This is optimally executed with low- to moderate-intensity aerobic or strength exercise. Adding a mindful component to a flexibility exercise, low-level cycling, slow intentional muscular contractions during strength training, or walking can be quite rewarding. He can also incorporate any of the select yoga poses described in the restorative or Iyengar tradition into the flexibility and strength-training components of the program. For example, inserting the seated or standing spinal twist pose, the child's pose, or cobra pose between resistance-training exercises may increase flexibility and serve as a welcome period of relative rest and energy restoration. It is imperative that proper yogic breathing accompany these exercises. The popular tree pose can be included as part of a circuit of exercises to help stimulate balance control. Finally, you can introduce a simple breathing exercise to each workout, which many clients find therapeutic.

Chapter 14: Exercise and Special Populations

Expand Your Knowledge

I.   (a) Poor diet; (b) Physical inactivity; (c) Smoking
II.   (a) have been cleared by their personal physicians; (b) Metabolic syndrome; (c) Malignant; benign; (d) osteoporosis; weightbearing exercise
III.   (a) D; (b) I; (c) D; (d) D; (e) D
IV.   (c) Aerobic endurance and weight training in combination has been shown to effectively burn calories and maintain fat-free mass and resting metabolic rate, producing the best long-term weight-loss results.
V.   (a) 1, 4; (b) 5; (c) 1; (d) 1, 2, 3
VI.   Unsupported forward flexion; twisting at the waist with turned feet, especially when carrying a load; lifting both legs simultaneously while in the prone or supine position; rapid movements such as twisting, forward flexion, or hyperextension
VII.   (a) Mode: The initial mode should consist of low-intensity endurance exercise, gradually progressing to moderate-intensity exercise utilizing interval-type training. The resistance-training program should utilize one set of 12 to 15 repetitions of eight to 10 exercises. (b) Intensity: Begin at an intensity of 40 to 50% of heart-rate reserve, an RPE of 9 to 11 (6 to 20 scale), or a heart rate 20 to 30 beats over resting heart rate. (c) Duration: Total duration should be gradually increased

to 30 minutes or more of continuous or interval training, plus additional time for warm-up and cool-down activities. (d) Clients should perform three to five days per week of aerobic training and two days per week of resistance training.

VIII. (a) 2, 5, 6; (b) 3; (c) 1, 4

IX. (a) Osteoarthritis is a degenerative disease of the joint cartilage, while rheumatoid arthritis is a chronic and systemic inflammatory disease. (b) Type 1 diabetes is caused by the destruction of insulin-producing cells, which occurs in childhood, while type 2 diabetes usually occurs during adulthood in overweight individuals and initially presents as insulin resistance. Increasing numbers of children are being diagnosed with type 2 diabetes. (c) An ischemic stroke occurs when blood supply to the brain is cut off, while a hemorrhagic stroke occurs when a blood vessel in the brain bursts. (d) LDL is the major carrier of cholesterol in the blood and is often called the "bad" cholesterol, while HDL is called the "good" cholesterol, as high HDL levels are associated with a reduced risk of coronary artery disease. (e) Fibromyalgia is a syndrome characterized by long-lasting widespread pain and tenderness at specific points on the body, while chronic fatigue syndrome is a debilitating and complex illness characterized by profound, incapacitating fatigue lasting at least six months.

X. Spinal flexion, crunches, and rowing machines; jumping and high-impact aerobics; trampolines and step aerobics; abducting or adducting the legs against resistance; pulling on the neck with the hands behind the head

XI. (a) Sudden numbness or weakness in the face, arms, or legs; (b) Sudden confusion or trouble speaking or understanding others; (c) Sudden trouble seeing in one or both eyes; (d) Sudden walking problems, dizziness, or loss of balance or coordination; (e) Sudden severe headache with no known cause

Multiple-choice Questions

(1) A; (2) D; (3) D; (4) A; (5) C; (6) B; (7) C; (8) A; (9) B; (10) B

Show What You Know

I. (a) Reduce the outdoor ride to 60 minutes at a reduced intensity. (b) Change high-impact to low-impact and cycle indoors in an air-conditioned environment. (c) Reduce low-impact aerobics from three times per week to twice per week and cycle only 45 minutes.

II. (a) Mode: Sustained activities that use large muscle groups. Incorporate fun activities that develop other components of fitness. Encourage Ima to live an active lifestyle. (b)

Intensity: Begin with low-intensity activity and gradually progress. As her conditioning improves, Ima should be encouraged to participate in moderate- and vigorous-intensity activities. Activities that encompass all three intensity zones are an excellent choice. (c) Duration: Ima should accumulate 60 minutes or more of daily physical activity. (d) Frequency: Ima should be encouraged to exercise daily. (e) Strength-training: Strength-training activities should be performed at least three days per week. They do not need to be structured and can be incorporated into games and other activities.

Chapter 15: Common Musculoskeletal Injuries and Implications for Exercise

Expand Your Knowledge

I. (a) strains; (b) sprains; (c) menisci; (d) mechanical back pain; degenerative disc disease; sciatica

II. (a) Muscle fatigue; (b) Fluid and electrolyte depletion; (c) Forced knee extension while the foot is dorsiflexed; (d) Forced dorsiflexion while the knee is extended

III. (a) Weightbearing as tolerated; no splinting/casting; isometric exercises; full range of motion; strengthening/stretching exercises as tolerated; (b) Immobilization with air splint; physical therapy; range of motion, stretching; strengthening exercises; (c) Immobilization; physical therapy over a longer period; possible surgical reconstruction

IV. (a) 2; (b) 4; (c) 3; (d) 1

V. (a) 2; (b) 1; (c) 3

VI. (a) The inflammatory phase can last up to six days, depending on the severity of the injury. The focus of this phase is to immobilize the injured area and begin the healing process. Increased blood flow occurs to bring in oxygen and nutrients to rebuild the damaged tissue. (b) The second phase is the fibroblastic/proliferation phase, which begins approximately at day 3 and lasts approximately until day 21. This phase begins with the wound filling with collagen and other cells, which will eventually form a scar. Within two to three weeks, the wound can resist normal stresses, but wound strength continues to build for several months. (c) The maturation/remodeling phase, which begins approximately at day 21, can last up to two years. This phase begins the remodeling of the scar, rebuilding of bone, and/or restrengthening of tissue into a more organized structure.

VII. Pain, redness, swelling, warmth, loss of function

VIII. Is the client appropriate for exercise or should he or she be cleared by a medical professional?

IX. P = Protection; R = rest or restricted activity; I = Ice; C = Compression; E = Elevation

X. (a) Pain in the affected area; restrictions from the client's doctor; prolonged immobilization of muscle and connective tissue; joint swelling from trauma or disease; presence of osteoporosis or rheumatoid arthritis; a history of prolonged steroid use; (b) A fracture site that is healing; acute soft-tissue injury; post-surgical conditions; joint hypermobility; an area of infection

XI. (a) 2; (b) 3; (c) 1; (d) 4

XII. (a) 2; (b) 1; (c) 4; (d) 3

XIII. (a) Heavy lifting, pushing, and pulling with twisting of the spine; (b) Prolonged static postures; (c) Obesity; (d) Stress or depression; (e) Poor physical fitness; (f) Inherited disease; (g) Smoking; (h) Pregnancy; (i) Other diseases (e.g., osteoarthritis, rheumatoid arthritis, ankylosing spondylitis, cancer)

XIV. (a) 2; (b) 4; (c) 7; (d) 1; (e) 10; (f) 6; (g) 5; (h) 11; (i) 9; (j) 3; (k) 8; (l) 12

XV. (a) Get fitted for footwear toward the end of the day. (b) Allow a space up to the width of the index finger between the end of the longest toe and the end of the shoe. (c) The ball of the foot should match the widest part of the shoe, and the client should have plenty of room for the toes to wiggle without experiencing slippage in the heel. (d) Shoes should not rub or pinch any area of the foot or ankle. (e) The client should wear the same weight of socks that he or she intends to use during the activity.

Multiple-choice Questions

(1) C; (2) D; (3) B; (4) A; (5) C; (6) D; (7) A; (8) B; (9) C; (10) A

Show What You Know

I. While it is true that running on soft surfaces can be easy on the joints of the lower body because of a dampening of the ground-reaction forces, running on too soft of a surface (e.g., sand or plush grass) can introduce a level of instability that may actually increase injury potential. These uneven surfaces appear to place an excessive challenge on the foot and ankle to maintain whole-body balance while running. Some research has shown an increased risk of Achilles tendon issues when running on sand surfaces compared to running

on asphalt, which was deemed safer. The following tips can help protect the client's lower extremities when she runs on soft, uneven surfaces:
- Wear an athletic shoe with good motion control
- Supplement running workouts with exercises that dynamically strengthen the foot and ankle joints (e.g., calf raises performed on a wobble board or a BOSU™)
- Avoid soft/uneven surfaces if the client has a history of lower-extremity problems, especially involving the ankle joint

II. (a) The overhead press can be modified so that the exerciser only moves through a limited range of motion. The shoulders should also be positioned more toward the front of the body, in the scapular plane. (b) The client should bend the elbow slightly to reduce the torque on the healing muscles. (c) Range of motion should be limited to 45 degrees of knee flexion, with a gradual progression to 90 degrees as tolerated. (d) Have the client do a straight-leg raise in a sitting or supine position.

Chapter 16: Emergency Procedures

Expand Your Knowledge

I. The PAR-Q can help identify high-risk individuals who need medical referral or require modifications to their exercise programs. It can also help identify the need for additional qualified staff members if there are a number of high-risk clients.

II. (a) The name of the victim; (b) The date and time of the incident; (c) What happened; (d) What was done to care for the victim and by whom; (e) Names, addresses, and phone numbers of witnesses

III. A = Airway; B = Breathing; C = Circulation; s = Severe bleeding

IV. (a) In this situation, implied consent can be assumed. The trainer should proceed by checking for the ABCs. (b) Tilt the head back and lift the chin to move the tongue away from the back of the throat. Check for breathing by looking at the chest and listening and feeling for breath. (c) The trainer should give two breaths into the mouth of the victim while pinching the nose. (d) Without a pulse, the victim will need immediate CPR, starting with chest compressions.

V. (a) To address any issues that are not immediately life-threatening. (b) The victim is conscious and speaking, or is unconscious with stable ABCs. (c) Skin that is warm and

ACE Personal Trainer Master the Manual

has a pinkish tone indicates adequate blood flow and oxygenation, whereas grayish, pale skin may indicate poor circulation.

VI. It is appropriate to call EMS when there is a life-threatening situation or anything that requires immediate medical attention, such as a person who is not breathing, has an open wound to the chest, or is bleeding profusely

VII. (a) X; (c) X; (d) X; (e) X

VIII. (a) What is your emergency? (b) Where is your emergency and what number are you calling from? (c) What is your name? (d) Is the victim conscious? (e) Is the victim breathing normally? (f) Are you able to assist with CPR? (g) Do you have access to an AED?

IX. (a) Early access; (b) Early CPR; (c) Early defibrillation; (d) Early advanced care

X. In "hands-only CPR," a bystander only needs to remember to push hard and fast on the center of the victim's chest until trained help arrives. This is effective for victims who are adults and who have been witnessed going into cardiac arrest. When the collapse is witnessed and CPR begins immediately, the victim's blood still contains oxygen and oxygen remains in the lungs. By pumping the chest, this oxygenated blood can be distributed to the body.

XI. (a) Heart attacks begin with chest pain called angina pectoris, which is described as chest pressure or a squeezing feeling, which may be mistaken for heart burn. This pain can also travel to one or both arms (typically the left arm, as the heart is on the left side of the chest), the neck, jaw, shoulder, or stomach. The back may also be affected. Shortness of breath may accompany these symptoms, and they may even take place without any chest pain. Nausea, a cold sweat, and lightheadedness may also occur. For women, the most common symptom is also chest pain, but women are more likely than men to experience nausea, shortness of breath, and back or jaw pain. (b) If the right hemisphere of the brain is affected by a stroke, the signs and symptoms will appear on the right side of the face but the left side of the body due to the crossing over of cranial nerves. This can cause a facial droop on the right side, weakness or paralysis on the left side of the body, vision problems, memory loss, and a quick, inquisitive type of behavior. (c) The onset of hypoglycemia may be rapid and can be displayed as headache, hunger, weakness, sweating, or fatigue. (d) A tonic clonic seizure usually starts with an "aura"—the person experiences a smell or sound that indicates a seizure is about to occur. When the seizure starts, the victim experiences a

loss of consciousness and whole-body jerking movements (i.e., tonic clonic movements), where the muscles contract and relax, the jaw is clenched, and bowel or bladder control might be lost. This could last one or more minutes, and is followed by a state of exhaustion called the postictal state. The victim may still be unconscious in this state for 10 to 30 minutes. (e) The signs and symptoms of shock include restlessness; anxiety; altered mental status; pale, cool, and clammy skin; fast and weak pulse; irregular breathing; nausea; and thirst.

XII. To care for a victim of heat stroke, call EMS if the person displays any abnormal signs, such as confusion, vomiting, inability to drink, red hot and dry skin due to an inability to sweat, shallow breathing, seizures, or unresponsiveness. Cool the victim immediately—do not wait for EMS to arrive. Get the person into a shady area, remove any tight clothing, and apply ice packs to areas of high blood flow such as the groin, axilla (armpit), and neck or submerge the victim in a tub of ice water. If the person can swallow, it is safe to give him or her cool fluids to drink, but not if the person is vomiting, is confused or unresponsive, or has had a seizure. Monitor the ABCs and core temperature. Once the person's behavior is back to normal, stop the cooling so that a state of hypothermia does not develop.

XIII. (a) Clear the area so the victim will not hit his or her head on nearby furniture or objects. (b) Place a towel under the victim's head to help protect it from injury. (c) Never restrain the victim or place anything in the victim's mouth. (d) Have someone phone EMS.

XIV. (a) Amnesia; (b) Confusion; (c) Memory loss; (d) Headache; (e) Drowsiness; (f) Loss of consciousness; (g) Impaired speech; (h) Tinnitus; (i) Unequal pupil size; (j) Nausea; (k) Vomiting; (l) Balance problems or dizziness; (m) Blurry or double vision; (n) Sensitivity to light or noise; (o) Any change in the individual's behavior, thinking, or physical functioning

XV. Rescuers should wear gloves, use a protective barrier device when performing CPR, and, if there is potential for blood to splash on the rescuer, a gown and eye protection should also be worm.

XVI. R = Rest or restricted activity; Rest or restricted activity is necessary to allow the body to heal. I = Ice; Ice should be applied for approximately 20 minutes to relieve swelling and pain. C = Compression; Compression bandages help prevent swelling and should be applied distally and wrapped proximally. E = Elevation; Elevating the injury above the level of the heart can help reduce swelling.

Multiple-choice Questions
(1) C; (2) A; (3) D; (4) B; (5) C; (6) D; (7) C; (8) A; (9) B; (10) D

Show What You Know
I. (a) Tip is most likely having a hypoglycemic reaction. Check the airway, breathing, and circulation. Active the EMS system. Protect the victim and prevent injury in case of a seizure. Do not give anything by mouth. (b) First, activate the EMS system. Attempt to place a barrier between you and any wounds or blood by wearing rubbers gloves or grabbing a towel or shirt. Next, apply direct pressure to the wounds and elevate the arms above the heart. If others are available, ask if they can obtain rubber gloves or another barrier so they can apply pressure to the wounds or to other pressure points at the brachial site. Do not apply a tourniquet, as pressure and elevation should stop the bleeding until help arrives. Try to get the victim to calm down through reassurance. Help the paramedics when they arrive. Because you have been showered with blood, you need to wash your entire body with soap and running water. Any objects that have come in contact with blood (glass, clothes) must be contained and properly washed or disposed of.

Chapter 17:
Legal Guidelines and Professional Responsibilities

Expand Your Knowledge
I. (a) A 50-50 partnership can result in a stalemate because neither partner can institute policy without permission of the other, since business decisions must be approved by a majority (50.1%) of the owners. (b) Because the minority partner in a 60-40 split is only entitled to 40% of profits and can be outvoted on any organizational issue, he or she would be less likely to invest as much money. (c) One partner my not understand or fully appreciate the importance of the others partner's duties or activities.
II. (a) An express partnership is created by a contract between the parties, while an implied partnership can be created and recognized by the judicial system if individuals act as partners (such as by sharing a checking account or signing jointly for a business loan). (b) A general partner

typically retains personal liability, while a limited partner is only liable for his or her direct financial contribution. (c) S-corps are the most "typical" type of corporation used by personal-training businesses that do not operate as a sole proprietorship or partnership, and they can have a maximum of 100 investors, all of whom must be from the United States. It is highly unlikely that any personal-training business will ever create a C-corp, which is structured to seek investors and conduct business around the world. (d) Flow-through taxation is a benefit of many types of business structures; profits are taxed at lower personal rates rather than higher corporate rates and yearly losses can flow-through to be used by owners to offset profits from other income. Double taxation is a disadvantage of C-corps, which are taxed as a company first, before shareholders pay taxes on their individual dividends.

III.

Type	Advantage	Disadvantage
Sole proprietorship	Easily created and managed Flow-through taxation	Personal liability Raising capital
Partnership	Easily created Flow-through taxation	Potential management disputes Personal liability (except limited partners)
S-corps	Flow-through taxation Limited liability	Limited number of potential investors Costs of formation and operation
LLC/LLP	Flow-through taxation Limited liability	Undefined operating standards in states
C-corps	Limited liability Unlimited number of investors	Costs of formation and operation Double taxation

IV. (a) The upfront costs for the franchise fee and the ongoing costs to maintain the association with the parent brand of the franchise; (b) The annual costs of maintaining the franchise, which include making necessary purchases through the franchise system; (c) An association with a particular brand, which could be a drawback if other franchisees within the network perform badly or conduct unethical business practices; (d) The fact that the franchisee agrees to follow the franchise's operating model, which could limit the franchisee's ability to adapt to changing market forces

V. (a) Work details; (b) Payment; (c) Length of relationship; (d) Training and retraining; (e) Equipment; (f) Number of clients; (g) Nature of the work; (h) Intention of the parties

VI.   (a) IC; (b) E; (c) IC; (d) E; (e) E; (f) IC; (g) IC; (h) E

VII.   (a) An offer and acceptance with a mutual agreement of terms; (b) Consideration (an exchange of valuable items, such as money for services); (c) Legality (acceptable form under the law); (d) Ability of the partners to enter into a contract with respect to legal age and mental capacity

VIII.   (a) An act of omission is a form of negligence in which a personal trainer fails to act, while an act of commission is a form of negligence in which a personal trainer acts inappropriately. (b) Contributory negligence laws prevent a plaintiff in a lawsuit who has played some role in the injury from receiving *any* remuneration, while comparative negligence, which is used by most states, states that when multiple parties may have caused injuries, the court will apportion guilt and any subsequent award for damages. (c) General supervision involves watching a group of people, such as when a group fitness instructor watches a large class. Specific supervision occurs when an individual is supervised performing a specific activity, such as what typically occurs in a one-on-one personal-training session. (d) An umbrella liability policy provides added coverage for all of the other insurance that a person may have in place, while vicarious liability states that employers are responsible for the actions of their employees.

IX.   (b) X; (c) X

X.   (a) Point out to the client that the shoes may not be right for her and that quality fitness shoes should not require a break-in period. (b) Stop using worn, frayed, or potentially dangerous equipment. Instead of a verbal statement, express your concern in writing and keep a copy for your files. (c) Do not allow the neighbor to join in on the run. After a health-history screening, a waiver of liability, and, in some cases, physician's approval have been obtained, the neighbor would be able to join if the 5-mile run was appropriate for his or her ability level. (d) Do not use these cards unless you are a licensed doctor. Change "exercise prescriptions" to "exercise programs."

XI.   (a) Trainers should ensure that floor surfaces will cushion the feet, knees, and legs from excessive stress. (b) There should be sufficient free space available to protect the client from other patrons and from hurting him- or herself on equipment. (c) Functional lighting must be sufficient for the chosen exercises. (d) There must be functional heating and air conditioning systems. (e) Proximity to drinking fountains and bathrooms is important for some clients.

XII.   (a) Risk identification; (b) Risk evaluation; (c)

Selection of an approach for managing each risk; (d) Implementation; (e) Evaluation

Multiple-choice Questions

(1) B; (2) C; (3) D; (4) B; (5) A; (6) C; (7) A; (8) B; (9) D; (10) D

Show What You Know

I.   (a) Argument for the plaintiff—In this case, the plaintiff will probably choose to focus on the point of law known as negligence. Mr. Weeble will try to establish that Doug should not have approved the two pieces of glued wood as suitable workout equipment. The plaintiff will then try to establish that he has indeed suffered an injury, and that the improper material and exercise recommendation led to the injury. (b) Argument for the defendant—In this case, the defendant would try to establish that the plaintiff knew the inherent risks of the exercise prior to the accident and that the plaintiff selected the piece of wood knowing it would be placed under the heels during the exercise. (c) The judge would probably settle the case in favor of the plaintiff because it would seem that the defendant had a duty to properly supervise the plaintiff's workouts, which he did not fulfill. Also, the injury that was sustained was directly caused by the improper use of equipment and an exercise recommendation made by the defendant. (d) Avoid the use of homemade props or equipment.

Chapter 18: Personal-training Business Fundamentals

Expand Your Knowledge

I.   (a) E; (b) C; (c) C; (d) E; (e) C; (f) E; (g) E; (h) E; (i) C; (j) C

II.   A suburban facility will generally have members coming in before work, stay-at-home parents or retirees who visit during the day, youth in the afternoon, and people who exercise in the evening before heading home, while an urban location will experience the highest number of visits in the morning before work, during lunch time, and right after work—with extremely slow periods in between.

III.   Some facilities will prosecute trainers for shoplifting or trespassing if they are caught training under the table. In addition, the trainer may lose his or her ACE credential, as this practice is illegal and unethical, and therefore a violation of the ACE Code of Ethics.

IV.   The best option is often to work as an employee at a health club or other fitness facility. These facilities are always adding new members, so they provide a steady stream of potential clients, and will give the trainer some of the experience needed to operate a fitness business without investing exorbitant time and money. These employers often provide training on how to market ones' skills and make sales. Health clubs are often involved in community projects, which can give the trainer an opportunity to work with the public and raise his or her profile in the community. Finally, these facilities sometimes provide their employees with opportunities to appear in local media talking about fitness-related topics.

V. (a) Executive summary: A brief outline of the business and an overview of how the business fills a need within the marketplace; (b) Business description: The details for the business as outlined in the executive summary, including the mission statement, business model, current status of the market, how the business fills a need within the market, and the management team; (c) Marketing plan: Specifies how prospective clients become paying clients; (d) Operational plan: Describes the structure for how a business will operate, including an organizational chart that identifies key decision makers and the employees responsible for executing those decisions; (e) Risk analysis: Reviews the risks involved in owning and operating the business, including barriers to entry and financial, competitive, and staffing issues; (f) Decision-making criteria: Includes a detailed cost-benefit analysis that demonstrates that the expenses for operating the business are worth the financial risks involved with establishing operations

VI. (a) Business description; (b) Executive summary; (c) Decision-making criteria; (d) Executive summary; (e) Business description; (f) Marketing plan; (g) Risk analysis; (h) Operational plan; (i) Risk analysis

VII. The first goal is to collect information about the client to screen for health risks and design an exercise program for his or her specific needs and abilities. The second goal is to give the potential client an opportunity to experience a specific brand of training so he or she can understand how working with a trainer will help him or her achieve fitness goals safely.

VIII. (a) The more people a trainer can meet during a work shift, the more familiar members will become with that trainer. The familiarity will lead to a rapport based on trust and communication, which can lead to the gaining of new clients. (b) Small-group training lowers the cost for each client and allows for camaraderie among participants, which improves motivation and adherence. It also gives the client a chance to "try out" personal training without making a large financial commitment. (c) Earning a group fitness instructor certification and leading classes enables the trainer to establish him- or herself as an "expert" in the eyes of participants and allows the trainer to build rapport with potential clients. (d) A trainer can set up a system whereby a client who does not cancel any sessions during the training program wins a free T-shirt with the trainer's brand or logo. That client then becomes a great advertising opportunity for the trainer.

IX. (a) The level of experience that the potential business owner has in the fitness industry; (b) The level of self-motivation; (c) The ability to create and execute a business plan; (d) The size of the proposed business; (e) The location of the proposed business; (f) The cost of running the proposed business; (g) The structure of the proposed business

Multiple-choice Questions
(1) C; (2) D; (3) A; (4) C; (5) B; (6) C; (7) A; (8) B; (9) A; (10) D

Show What You Know
I. $60,000/50 weeks per year = $1,200 per week
$1,200 per week/$40 per session = 30 sessions each week

II. Monthly fitness floor income: 20 hours per week x $12 per hour = $240/week x 4 weeks/month = $960/month
Remaining income to be earned: $3,000 – $960 = $2,040
Number of sessions per month: $2,040/$20 per session = 102 sessions/month
Number of sessions per day: 102 sessions per month/4 weeks = 25.5 sessions per week/5 days per week = 5.1 sessions/day
Weekly hours = 20 hours on the fitness floor + 25.5 hours of personal training = 45.5 hours/week